3 =

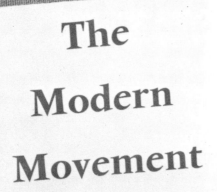

Cyril Connolly's
ONE HUNDRED MODERN BOOKS
From England, France and America 1880-1950

Catalog by Mary Hirth with an Introduction by Cyril Connolly

An Exhibition: March - December 1971

The Humanities Research Center · The University of Texas at Austin

Introduction to the Exhibit

By Cyril Connolly

I Suppose this Exhibition makes me one of the few writers who have seen their dream implemented by reality, who have rubbed a magic lamp and beheld a huge djinn turn the contents of an imaginary bookcase into the living word, the word made flesh through phot[...]phs, letters, manuscripts, association copies, so th[...]ry error of judgment is magnified as well as every [...] guess, making clearer every secret influence or [...]cted affinity. Only the University of Texas has [...] th[...] will and the means and the erudition to rais[...] [...]s memorial to the writers of our time, and I hope it [...] bring new hope and happiness and inspiration to ev[...]ne who loves literature and who owes a debt to thes[...]e-enhancing writers.

I would like to say som[...]ng about how this book, originally titled *One Hund[...] Key Books in the Modern Movement* and not *The M[...]rn Movement*, which would have been presumptuou[...] a checklist, nor *The Hundred Best Books*, since a "be[...]ook" implies other criteria than "key," came into being. One must first go back to my schooldays, when, an only child in rebellion against a conventional home and an even more conventional classical education, I first came to awareness. My adolescence, 1918–23, coincided with a larger first-war phenomenon. I was, without knowing it, in search of a father—or father-replacement. This search for a sympathetic spiritual authority is one of the least understood yet most persistent of the emotional drives, though it is common enough in other gregarious animals. A French teacher at school raised a corner of the curtain on Villon, Verlaine, Mallarmé, Baudelaire, but the cult of Flecker, Housman, and the Georgians still lay heavy. It was not until I got to Oxford in 1922 that I met a young don who shared my love of literature and who introduced me to the contemporary ferment. That is why this book is dedicated to Maurice Bowra, through whom I came to love and appreciate early Eliot, later Yeats, Edith Sitwell, E. M. Forster, Proust, and Valéry. Later on I went to work for Logan Pearsall Smith (another father) who made it possible for me to spend a winter in Paris (1928). There I fell in love with an American girl whom I found reading Ronald Firbank, and there I met Sylvia Beach, who introduced me to Joyce, Gide and Hemingway. I identified with the Paris-American pack and was accepted by them, writing some of the first articles on Hemingway, *Finnegans Wake*, and the Surrealists for *Life and Letters* and *The New Statesman*. Even as I read and got to know these Paris expatriates, I came to see them as part of the explosion of my own emotional life as I wooed and married my American girl, Frances

4

Jean Bakewell of Baltimore, then in her nineteenth year. Joyce and Hemingway, Cummings and Fitzgerald, *transition* and Sylvia Beach joined up with Eliot, Yeats, Huxley, the Sitwells and Wyndham Lewis and with the great succession of French writers, Baudelaire, Flaubert, Proust and Valéry to form the Olympus from which this book came to be chosen. The one great gap was Pound, whom I did not come upon till Sylvia Beach—once more—introduced me to his *Mauberley* many years later—*mea sola et sera voluptas*, my late and only pleasure. I write of these personal feelings to try to show what an upheaval lies behind my passion for poetry, of which this list is merely the distant echo. Many new writers became my friends; Evelyn Waugh, Elizabeth Bowen, Auden, Spender, Isherwood, Dylan Thomas, but none have been quite so able to alleviate the heart's hunger or the irrecoverable intensity of the year 1928 and the winter/spring of 1929, of 12 Rue de l'Odéon, 30 Rue de Vaugirard, when I found myself at the hub of three cultures.

I wrote a whole book, *The Unquiet Grave*, round that profound experience; I rather wished someone else might suggest it should have been included in *The Hundred Books*, particularly in view of its extensive quotations from many authors in this selection, but not a hope. In fact the *One Hundred Key Books* met with a frigid reception from most reviewers and has had to make its way chiefly through booksellers' catalogues. "First they'll crab you, then they'll crib you," as Desmond MacCarthy used to say. This treatment might have been expected for a very idiosyncratic anthology but in fact I have tried very hard to be objective, weighing the claims of country against country, group against group, and allowing for my own

weak spots. My worst defect is a blind eye for the grand, an inability to swallow larger than life extravaganzas on a colossal scale. I could reel off a long list but here I will mention some of the most significant. Dreiser, *An American Tragedy*; Gertrude Stein, *The Making of Americans*; Wyndham Lewis, *The Apes of God;* e. e. cummings, *The Enormous Room*; Claudel, *The Satin Slipper;* St. John Perse, *Anabasis*; Faulkner, Thomas Wolfe, Malcolm Lowry, James Agee, Djuna Barnes, Jules Romains, Roussel, Henry Miller (most regretfully). On the other hand I have included one or two very slight books which should perhaps have made way for some of these titans and twice my judgment has been at fault. I decided on 1880 as the beginning and 1950 as the terminus; even so 1950, which is marked by the deaths of Shaw and Orwell, with Dylan Thomas's soon to follow, is perhaps too arbitrary.

It meant excluding several writers who should really have been in, such as Beckett, Anthony Powell and Robert Lowell. Beckett would have to have been included on the strength of *Murphy* (1938), with *Watt* on the borderline; *Waiting for Godot* was not yet published. It seemed to me that only the last would have merited his inclusion. Anthony Powell's earlier comic novels, even *From a View to a Death*, are nothing like as important as his novel-sequence, *The Music of Time*, which began with *A Question of Upbringing* (1951), and Robert Lowell's *Lord Weary's Castle* is still full of monotonous versification from which he only escapes in *Life Studies*, a far more significant book (1959).

I do not know if it is due to old age or to the overwhelming tempo of current events, but I form an impression of hurrying floodwaters carrying everything away in a muddy spate of torn trees, huts, hen roosts rushing past, of monuments of culture long buried and forgotten, even in the few years since this exhibition was planned and the book written. To compile lists and catalogues is an anxious occupation which suggests a morbid preoccupation with the flight of time. Flaubert, Joyce, Thomas Wolfe were dabs at it; Ezra the scribe, though not the poet, and I feel my list came just in time. Already a hundred new critical works have accumulated around the corpus of Eliot, Joyce, Yeats, Pound, Proust, Lawrence, Hemingway and even Auden, still so very much with the living. And yet literature, never so well taught as now, is perhaps never so little read; I mean that the literary experience, the shock of recognition, the cross-fertilization between minds of which this exhibition gives such wonderful examples, is severely threatened by the distraction of other media and by economic pressures. These writers, many of whom I knew, lived in an emptier world; no one saw Joyce on television or even heard him on the wireless, his voice survives on one gramophone record, Yeats also; though Eliot received modern coverage, we know nothing about Nathanael West or Hart Crane except from one or two snapshots; even a writer very famous in his time like George Moore is physically elusive, and the only man living who can imitate Proust (Paul Morand) is in his eighties. For this reason the association copy, which plays such a large part here, antedates the radio and television interview as a manifestation of personality, a chain reaction. Before the days of the media, writers were unselfconscious and did not "sit" to posterity or sign books for collectors. Hardly anyone collected them. They could also be poor and obscure, and there was no campus spread under them to

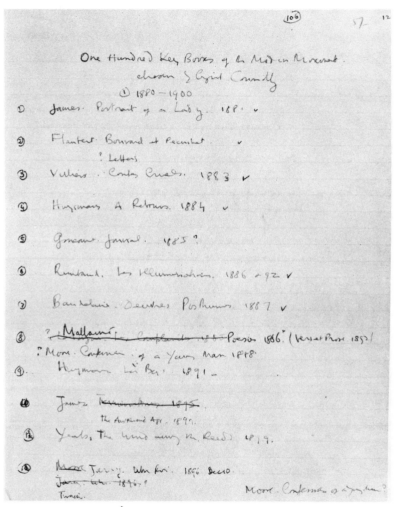

PAGE FROM CONNOLLY'S NOTEBOOK

FROM CYRIL CONNELLY, BUSHEY LODGE, FIRLE, LEWES, SUSSEX.
RIPE 245

Further Reading.
Bowra. Heritage of Symbolism + Creative Experiment   Gide Journal
Connolly. Enemies of Promise. Spender. Life and ... Art
(Stein. Autobiography of Alice B. Toklas (5 vols)
O. Sitwell. Left hand. right hand. (5 vols)
Wilson. wound + the Bow. Orwell. Inside the
Whale + Critical essays. Leavis. New Bearings in
Modern Poetry. Trilling. the Liberal Imagination.
Praz. the Romantic Agony.

POST CARD
THE ADDRESS TO BE WRITTEN ON THIS SIDE

... both grandly conceived

his lyrical feeling,
devotion to humanity,
respect for the
individual, broken
with a certain
mediterranean
detachment

It is
La Peste.   allegory
The Plague is an allegorical transposition
of the German occupation in terms of an
outbreak of plague at Oran. City, pestilence
and population are integrated round a small
group of social workers, doctor, priest, judge,
journalist, + two or three men of good will,
equivalent of a ... the Resistance. the
lyrical feeling, a devotion + respect for
humanity make this the least typical of the
... together with a certain Mediterranean detachment
littérature engagée — ...

CONNOLLY'S NOTES ON HIS PERSONAL POST CARDS

catch them if they fell. Apart from their powers as trailblazers, as architects of our own sensibility, I think this modest isolation is part of their beauty, even as Claudel recalled to Gide seeing Verlaine and Villiers "with destitution in their eyes."

For visitors who have not time for the introduction to *One Hundred Key Books* or its captions, I would like to repeat that I use the "modern movement" loosely to mean what we all know, but cannot define, the revolt against nineteenth century materialism: "The modern spirit was a combination of certain intellectual qualities inherited from the Enlightenment: lucidity, irony, scepticism, intellectual curiosity, combined with the passionate intensity and enhanced sensibility of the Romantics, their rebellion and sense of technical experiment, their awareness of living in a tragic age." The word "Modernity" was first used by the Goncourts, then Gautier. Technical experiment without imagination is not enough, but neither is imagination with an unimaginative attitude to form.

I suspect Robert Frost, Max Beerbohm, Galsworthy, Wilde of being anti-modernists and have left them out with many other traditional writers (Walter de la Mare, Kipling). I have not included translations from languages I do not know—German, Russian, even Italian and Spanish. Exceptions, Waley's *Chinese Poems*, Koestler's *Darkness at Noon* (first published in English). I have left out philosophy and other subjects whose frontiers march with literature. My method was to go through lists of books under the years they were published, from 1880–1950, and put together all the significant, then slowly weed them out. If some well-known book is not there, there is, I hope, some good reason. Of course any other fancier could make a different list; mine is only a rather pertinent suggestion. There are in fact more than a hundred books because I have included some pairs of slim volumes as one.

To come back to the exhibition, the embodiment of a dream, the incarnation of the dry bones of my catalogue, one would like it to exist in perpetuity like so many side chapels in a great cathedral, each with their images and ex-votos and paintings where the onlooker can meditate and time stands still. Hemingway's letter to David Garnett —what a treasure that is—; and Hart Crane's message to e. e. cummings to buy *A Survey of Modernist Poetry; The Waste Land* with its eliminated line "(The ivory men make company between us)," and many writers expressing their doubt and despair about books which are in fact seminal. I suppose no critic, bibliophile or maker of literary litany has had such satisfaction as the summoning to this exhibition of the living genius—as Mallarmé said of Debussy's setting to music of his *Après-midi d'un faune*: "Your illustration goes even further *dans la nostalgie et la lumière, avec finesse, avec malaise, avec richesse*"—in nostalgia and light, with subtlety, with inquietude, with luxury—may they in turn stimulate the visitor to go home and do better.

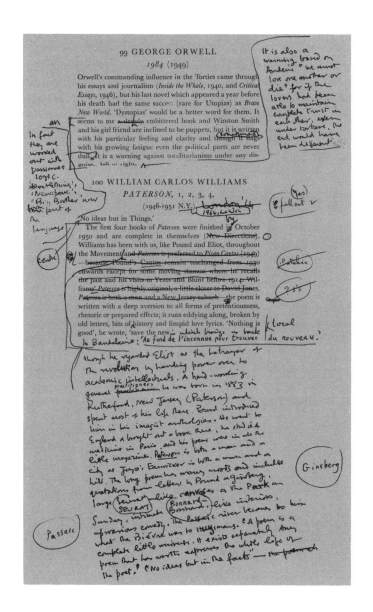

To The
Academic
Center
Library – gratefully
Cyril Connolly
March
67

CYRIL CONNOLLY, 1967

CYRIL CONNOLLY (b. 1903)

The Modern Movement: 100 Key Books from England, France and America, 1880–1950

A. First edition. London, 1965. Dust jacket.

B. First American edition. New York, 1966. Dust jacket.

C. Holograph manuscript in two notebooks, both signed by Connolly. The smaller of the two contains the author's preliminary lists by years with many titles, which eventually became final selections, underlined. The other also contains lists, but with titles numbered 1 through 100 and the final list in reverse, 100 through 1, so that titles may be seen in retrospect 1950 through 1880. Here too is the first draft of the text. Laid in are three postcards and one sheet of notepaper, all with holograph notes.

D. Holograph manuscript on notepaper and postcards. 37pp. 25 postcards.

E. Typescript, carbon copy, with the author's extensive holograph emendations. 64pp. n.d. Tan wrappers with typed label and holograph note in Connolly's hand: "MASTER Copy Please retype from this."

F. Galleys with the author's extensive emendations, holograph and typed. Printer's stamp: T. & A. Constable Ltd. Printers. Edinburgh, 2 July 1965. Holograph note: "—Proofs—Corrected by Cyril Connolly in his own hand. Feb 1966. Cyril C."

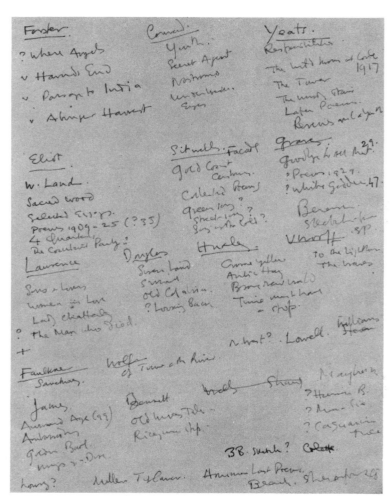

PAGE FROM CONNOLLY'S NOTEBOOK

1. HENRY JAMES (1843–1916)

The Portrait of a Lady (1881)

A. First edition. 3 volumes. London, 1881.

B. Limited edition. Baltimore, 1967.
Number 299 of 1950 copies made for the members of The Limited Editions Club by Irvin Silvers at The Garamond Press. Pastel illustrations by Colleen Browning. Signed by the artist.

C. Holograph letter signed by Joseph Conrad to James 16 October 1896. Conrad, a great admirer of James, expresses his pleasure in James' work: "I want to thank you for the charm of your words, the delight of your sentences, the beauty of your pages!" and adds that he is sending one of his books which he hopes James will accept "to augment the precious burden of my gratitude."

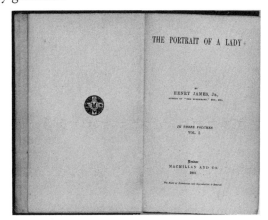

2. GUSTAVE FLAUBERT (1821–1880)

Bouvard et Pécuchet (1881 posthumous)

A. First edition. Paris, 1881.
One of 55 copies on *Hollande* sold without being numbered. Half maroon morocco, marbled boards and endpapers, tops gilt, other edges uncut.

B. Volume VII of the Complete Works. Paris, 1885.
Definitive edition based on the original manuscript. Introduction by Guy de Maupassant.

C. Translation. *Bouvard and Pecuchet*. New York, 1954. Dust jacket.
Put into English by T. W. Earp and G. W. Stonier. Introduction by Lionel Trilling, who hails the work as an act of defiance at the moment Flaubert "conceived to be the ultimate defeat of true culture," and asserts that although unfinished and unrevised it deserves, quite in its own right, to be placed with the great works of his canon. This edition includes Flaubert's *Dictionary of Accepted Ideas* translated with an introduction and notes by Jacques Barzun. From the library of Willard (Spud) Johnson, editor and publisher of the little magazine *The Laughing Horse,* with "Spud" on front free endpaper.

D. Holograph manuscript by Flaubert and some of his friends; used in the writing of the novel. 150pp. n.d.

E. Holograph letter signed by Flaubert to E. Laporte 15 September 1887 in which he mentions "*B. & P.*"

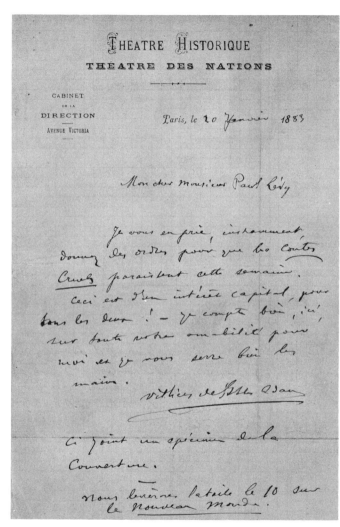

3A HOLOGRAPH LETTER FROM VILLIERS TO PAUL LEVY

3. VILLIERS DE L'ISLE-ADAM
(1838–1889)

Contes cruels (1883)

A. First edition. Paris, 1883.

Quarter green morocco, marbled boards and endpapers, original wrappers preserved, top edges gilt, others uncut, by Paul Vié. Bound in: holograph letter signed by Villiers to the publisher 20 January 1883 in which he pleads with him to see to it that *Contes cruels* appears that week, asserting that it is of the greatest importance for both of them. The letter includes Villier's layout for the front wrapper with complete details of typography, color, etc.

Another copy. Full red morocco, marbled endpapers, original wrappers preserved, gilt edges, and matching slip case by Alix.

B. Translation. *Cruel Tales.* London, 1963. Dust jacket. Put into English by Robert Baldick. Introduction by A. W. Raitt, who writes of Villier's style, its power and beauty, and his literary voice "which is unmistakably his own and which rings out as powerfully today as it did when he first raised it in protest against the abuses and errors of his time."

4. JORIS KARL HUYSMANS (1848–1907)

A *rebours* (1884)

A. First edition. Paris, 1884.
Half maroon morocco, marbled boards and endpapers, original wrappers preserved, top edges gilt, others uncut. Signature of L. Dorison, Professor of the Faculty of Letters, Dijon, on front wrapper.

B. Fourth edition. Paris, 1894.
Presentation copy inscribed to A. M. Glaser. Original wrappers.

C. Translation. *Against the Grain.* London, n.d.
Translator's name not given. Number 970 of 1000 copies.

D. Group of holograph cards signed by Huysmans to various individuals, various dates. He confirms 18 November 1866 a dinner appointment with Stéphane Mallarmé, suggesting they meet in a cafe patronized by business men rather than literary people, to whom he appears to have an aversion.

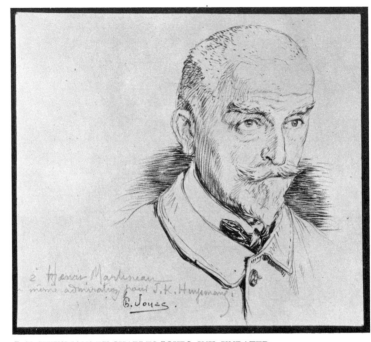

J. K. HUYSMANS BY CHARLES JOUDS. INK. UNDATED

5. CHARLES BAUDELAIRE (1821–1867)

Oeuvres posthumes (1887)

A. First edition. Paris, 1887.
Original wrappers.

B. Large paper copy. Paris, 1908.
Number 11 of 87 copies with the portrait in two states and the first printing of the articles from *Le Corsaire-Satan* and *Paris Journal* printed especially for M. le Docteur M. Laffont. Original wrappers.

C. Editions preferred by Cyril Connolly: *Écrits intimes*. Paris, 1946.
Introduction by Jean-Paul Sartre. Number 64 of 300 copies on *vélin*. Original wrappers.
Journaux intimes. Paris, 1949.
Edited by Jacques Crépet and Georges Blin. One of 75 copies on *Navarre*. Original wrappers.

D. Translation. *Intimate Journals*. London, 1930.
Put into English by Christopher Isherwood. Reproductions of Baudelaire's drawings. Introduction by T. S. Eliot. Number 40 of 400 copies of which 50 are bound in silk and signed by Eliot, who writes in his introduction that he found it difficult to estimate Baudelaire's worth, for although Baudelaire was in some ways far in advance of the point of view of his own time, he was very much of it and had a great part in forming a generation of poets after him.
Another copy. Blue cloth, unnumbered. Presentation copy inscribed by Eliot to his first wife: "For Vivienne Haigh Eliot from her husband T. S. Eliot. 1.10.30."

American edition. Hollywood, 1947. Dust jacket. Isherwood's translation with an introduction by W. H. Auden who also comments on Baudelaire's place in the development of poetry. He names Baudelaire and Poe as the fathers of modern poetry in that they were the first to be born into the new age, an age in which society is no longer based on tradition but is open to choice and change. Both men recognized this fact and accepted the challenge.

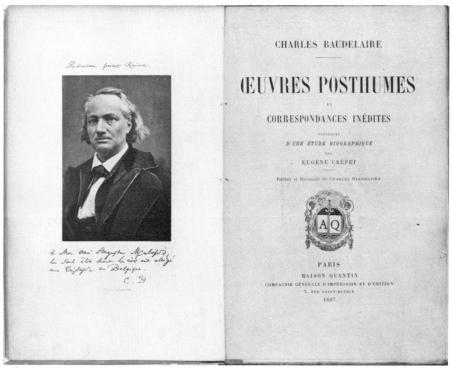

5A FIRST EDITION

6. ARTHUR RIMBAUD (1854–1891)

Les illuminations (1886)

A. First edition. Paris, 1886.
Notice by Paul Verlaine. Number 193 of 200 copies on *Hollande*. Inscribed by Verlaine to Raymond de la Tailhède, close friend of Rimbaud and Verlaine. Half red morocco, marbled boards and endpapers, original wrappers preserved.
Another copy. Number 194 of 200 copies on *Hollande*. Full crushed cyclamen levant with inlaid gold-stamped decoration, doublures and end leaves of vermilion suede, gilt edges, matching sleeve and slip case by Rose Adler.

B. Fourteenth edition. Paris, 1929.
A small book, somewhat worn, from the library of Edith Sitwell with her page jottings on front fly-leaf. Original wrappers.

C. Translation. *Illuminations.* London, 1932. Dust jacket. Put into English by Helen Rootham. Introductory essay by Edith Sitwell, who writes of the misery and destitution of Rimbaud's childhood, the intensity of his vision and powers and his gift for bringing all the attributes of the world together "regardless of Time and Place." Her own work, she points out, and that of Aldous Huxley and Gertrude Stein, among others, bear evidence of his great influence.

D. First edition. Les illuminations *et* Une saison en enfer *de Rimbaud.* Paris, 1927. By Ernest Delahaye.

One of seven copies on *Arches*. Quarter morocco, marbled endpapers, original wrappers preserved, top edges gilt, others uncut. Tipped in: original humorous drawing by Delahaye, a caricature of himself, Rimbaud, Germain Nouveau, and Verlaine.

E. Holograph manuscript with emendations by Isabelle Rimbaud. 16pp. [1914]. This essay appeared in *Mercure de France* under the title "Rimbaud mystique" and later in *Reliques* as "Rimbaud catholique: *Les Illuminations* et *La Chasse spirituelle.*"

F. Holograph manuscript in an unidentified hand quoting extracts from letters from Mlle. Rimbaud to M. Louis Pierquin concerning the unauthorized publication of *Les illuminations, Une saison en enfer* and *Reliquaire.* 4pp. n.d.

6D ORIGINAL HUMOROUS DRAWING BY DELAHAYE

7. STÉPHANE MALLARMÉ (1842–1898)

Poésies (1887)

A. First edition printed from type. Brussels, 1899.
One of 50 copies on *Japon imperial* with a bibliography not included in the 1887 facsimile edition. Original wrappers.
Another copy. Number 91 of 100 on *Hollande Van Gelder*, signed by the publisher. Red morocco, original wrappers preserved.

B. Translation. *Poems.* London, 1936.
Put into English by Roger Fry. Commentaries by Charles Mauron detailing the development of Mallarmé's style—a difficult style which begins with detachment from reality and continues through a series of modulations of all worldly experience and all gradations of dreams. One of the greatest obstacles to understanding Mallarmé, writes Mauron, is "a refusal to let ourselves go, a sort of stiffening of the mind."

C. Holograph letter signed by Mallarmé to an unidentified friend expressing his pleasure at the opportunity to see both his correspondent and Villiers de l'Isle-Adam.

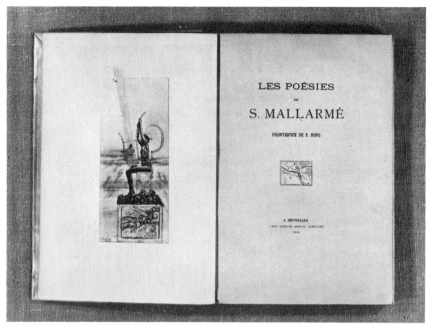

7A FIRST EDITION

GUY DE MAUPASSANT SELF-PORTRAIT. UNDATED

8. GUY DE MAUPASSANT (1850–1893)

Bel-ami (1885)

A. First edition. Paris, 1885.
Original wrappers.
Another copy. Half blue cloth, marbled boards, original wrappers preserved. Artine Artinian's copy with his bookplate.

B. Translation. *Bel-ami*. London, 1948. Dust jacket.
Put into English by Eric Sutton. Review copy, publisher's slip laid in. Artine Artinian's copy with his bookplate.

C. Group of holograph letters signed by Maupassant to his mother, father and various friends [1888–1890], several on "Bel-Ami" letterhead. In a letter to his mother dated only 7 July he comments on the reception of the novel, the sales of which he was trying to promote. At that date 13,000 had been sold. Maupassant anticipated 22,000, which he considered very commendable.

D. Holograph and typed replies to a questionnaire dated 30 July 1938 prepared by Artine Artinian and sent to contemporary novelists, short story writers and critics. Two questions are posed. The first concerns their reading of Maupassant, the second, Maupassant's place in the history of world literature. Replies shown are from William Carlos Williams, Booth Tarkington, William Saroyan and Wyndham Lewis.

9. EDMOND (1822–1896) and
JULES (1830–1870) DE GONCOURT

Journal des Goncourt (1887–1896)

A. Various impressions. Paris, 1888–1896. Volumes 4, 8 and 9 inscribed by Edmond de Goncourt. Quarter morocco, marbled boards and endpapers.

B. Translation. *The Goncourt Journals 1851–1870.* Garden City, New York, 1937.
Edited and translated with an introduction, notes and a biographical repertory by Lewis Galantière. Inscribed to [E. E.] Cummings by Galantière. Cummings' name and address embossed on half-title.
Pages from the Goncourt Journal. London, 1962. Dust jacket.
Edited and translated with an introduction by Robert Baldick. In the preface Edmond, the elder brother, writes of the intimacy between the two, the closeness which produced two minds receiving impressions so identical that the *Journal* may be considered as the "effusion of a single ego, of a single *I*." Baldick picks up the same theme in his introduction and calls attention to the uniqueness of a diary written by two men so different as these two, Edmond, "slow, serious and phlegmatic," Jules, eight years younger, "volatile, quick-witted and mischievous," yet achieving such a close integration of style that it is impossible to attribute with certainty any particular passage to one brother. Evelyn Waugh's copy with his bookplate.

C. Early page proofs, uncorrected. London, 1962.
Printed on one side of the paper only. Brown wrappers with printed label, stamped secret and confidential.

D. Typescript with a few holograph corrections, "Les Goncourt et le Journal" by Michel Puy, signed. 8pp. n.d. Puy, too, comments on the unusual collaboration of the brothers telling what they have seen and recounting what they have heard and in so doing bringing some order back into literature.

10. J. K. HUYSMANS (1848–1907)

Là-bas (1891)

A. First edition. Paris, 1891.
Huysmans' copy with his full-page holograph note concerning the Black Mass on front fly-leaf. Cloth, original wrappers preserved.
Another copy. Presentation copy inscribed to François Coppée. Half cloth, marbled boards and endpapers.

B. Translation. *Down There.* New York, 1924. Dust jacket.
Put into English by Keene Wallis.
Limited edition. Chicago, 1935.
Keene Wallis' translation. Frontispiece etching by John Groth. 850 copies for subscribers only.
Corrected edition. Evanston, 1958. Dust jacket.
Keene Wallis' translation with an introduction by Robert Baldick, Huysmans' biographer, in which he gives the historical background of *Là-bas*. The publisher notes that Wallis' translation has been carefully checked by Lucy Miller, who has corrected minor translation errors and printer's mistakes in the 1924 edition.

11H HOLOGRAPH LETTER FROM LUGNÉ-POE TO ALFRED JARRY

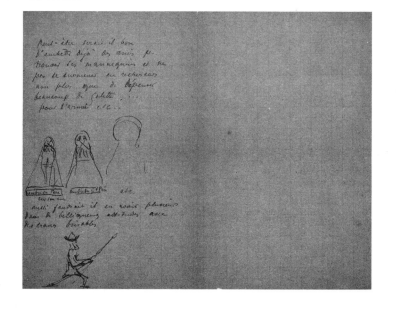

11. A L F R E D   J A R R Y (1873–1907)

Ubu roi (1896)

A. First edition. Paris, 1896.
Full brown mottled calf, marbled endpapers, original wrappers preserved, top edges gilt, others uncut.

B. First publication in two issues of Paul Fort's short-lived review *Le Livre d'Art* April and May 1896 bound in one volume.

C. Facsimile edition of the manuscript of Jarry and Claude Terrasse. Paris, 1897.
A drama in five acts with music by Claude Terrasse. Three-quarter crushed levant, raised bands, original wrappers preserved, tops gilt, other edges uncut. Number 3 of 10 large-paper copies on *Chine*. Signed in ink with the initials J. T. [Jarry Terrasse].

D. Illustrated edition. Paris, 1958.
Twenty original designs by André François. Review copy.

E. Translation. *Ubu Roi*. London, 1951. Dust jacket.
Put into English by Barbara Wright. Two portraits of the author by L. Lantier and F. A. Cazals, several drawings by Jarry and Pierre Bonnard printed in red on grey paper and 204 drawings by Franciszka Themerson, wife of Stefan Themerson, editor and publisher of the Gaberbocchus Press, doodled on litho plates and printed in black on yellow paper. In her introductory comments Miss Wright notes that Jarry thought of *Ubu roi* as something eternal. Although initially greeted with violent abuse as well as praise, in the half-century the play has been in existence it has not dated itself and at times seems even more topical today than in 1896. "It is timeless, placeless, it shamelessly displays what civilisation tries hard to hide." From the library of James Laughlin, publisher.

F. *The Ubu Plays*. London, 1968. Dust jacket.
Ubu Rex translated by Cyril Connolly and Simon Watson Taylor, *Ubu Cuckolded* by Cyril Connolly, *Ubu Enchained* by Simon Watson Taylor.

G. Twenty-one holograph letters and cards signed by Jarry to Lugné-Poe written mostly in 1896 when Jarry was serving as his secretary. Included is a letter dated 8 January 1896 in which Jarry outlines his views on the staging of the play. All are mounted on *Van Gelder* watermarked paper and bound together. Three-quarter deep gold morocco, marbled boards and endpapers by P. L. Martin.

H. Two holograph letters signed by Lugné-Poe to Jarry in which Lugné-Poe, who had become interested in producing the play, suggests they find some mannequins that can be dressed up as the ghosts, soldiers and nobles in order to keep expenses at a minimum. Sketches in the letters illustrate his ideas, n.d.

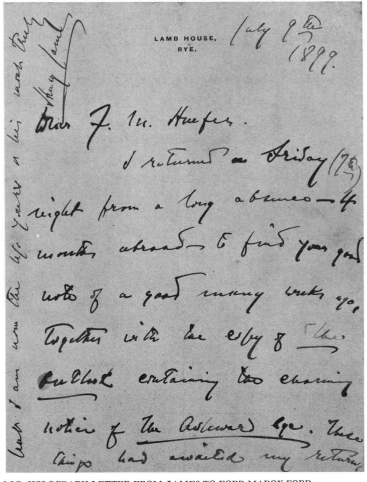

LAMB HOUSE,
RYE.

July 9th 1899.

Dear F. M. Hueffer.

I returned on Friday...

12C HOLOGRAPH LETTER FROM JAMES TO FORD MADOX FORD

12. HENRY JAMES (1843–1916)

The Awkward Age (1899)

A. First edition. London, 1899.
"Presentation Copy" blindstamped on title page. E. E. Cummings' name and address embossed on front endpaper with holograph initials M. M. C. [Marion Morehouse Cummings].

B. First American edition. New York, 1899.

C. Holograph letter signed by James to Ford Madox Ford 9 July 1899 thanking him for a copy of the *Outlook* containing a favorable review of the novel. James comments that he is "not pampered by the press" but he does not mind, for in his opinion it is "in general, on literary material, infantile."

13. ANDRÉ GIDE (1869–1951)

L'Immoraliste (1902)

A. First edition. Paris, 1902.
Presentation copy inscribed to Robert de Souza. Full brown morocco, green morocco doublures, original wrappers preserved, edges gilt, matching slip case by Noulhac.

B. Illustrated edition. Paris, 1925.
Illustration by René Ben-Sussan. Number 499 of 1100 copies on *vélin blanc Navarre*. Presentation copy inscribed to "Madame Knopf" [Mrs. Blanche W.]. Three-quarter navy morocco, marbled boards and endpapers, top edges gilt, others, uncut.

C. Translation. *The Immoralist*. New York, 1930.
Put into English by Dorothy Bussy.

D. Holograph manuscript by E. M. Forster, 6pp. n.d. Although the manuscript is untitled, the protective case is imprinted in gold, "André Gide: An Appreciation." Forster writes of his admiration for Gide, "Free minds are rare; perhaps even rarer than great minds," and of his belief that man ought at certain moments to turn against his conscience and "hit it hard on the head." This, writes Forster, is what Gide has done in the most disquieting of his novels, *L'Immoraliste*. In an accompanying note Forster indicates that he has no recollection of this particular manuscript, but that it may have been written for a Resistance paper and published, if at all, in French.

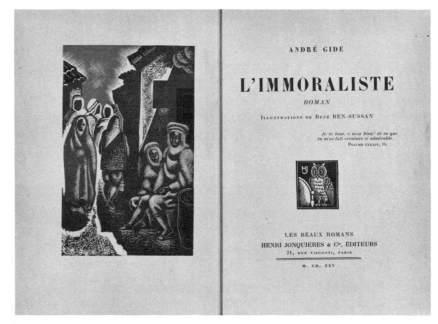

13B ILLUSTRATED EDITION

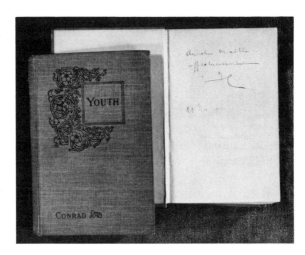

14. JOSEPH CONRAD (1857–1924)

Youth (1902)

A. First edition. Edinburgh and London, 1902.
Presentation copy inscribed to Henry James 20 November 1902. Pencil note beneath inscription, "Henry James's copy from Lamb House. H.J., Jr."

B. First American edition. New York, 1903.
Author's holograph note on front free endpaper, "1st U.S. Edition printed from unrevised proofs. Probably much nearer the Maga [*Blackwood's Magazine*] text than the 1st Eng. edition."

C. Fourteen holograph letters signed and two telegrams from Conrad to Henry Davray 1908–1912. In these letters to his French translator Conrad explains himself and his method of writing, saying that the reason his work is so difficult to translate is that unlike a *national* writer like Kipling who writes *of* his compatriots, he writes *for* them. The *national* writer's interest is *in the subject* while his own is *in the effect he produces.* [Italics Conrad's.] He makes a critical self-evaluation: "Here's how I judge myself: I say nothing new; I approach no problem; I am neither clever nor very eloquent. I have a certain feeling for far-off things, a taste for analyzing simple emotions and a turn of phrase that strikes the English. Please note that I do not say which *pleases.* I don't believe I please anyone here. I make an impression on some. . . . And that's where I am after the twelfth volume and in the fiftieth year of my life."

Conrad advises Davray not to forget that in spite of the favor he has been accorded in England he writes idiomatic English and his thoughts will emerge far better in idiomatic French than in literal translation.

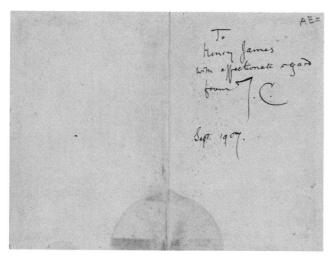

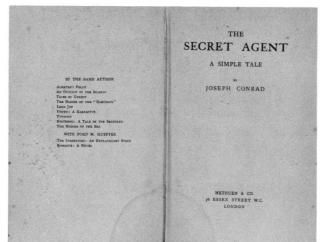

15. JOSEPH CONRAD (1857–1924)

The Secret Agent (1907)

A. First edition. London, 1907.
   Presentation copy inscribed: "To Henry James with affectionate regard from J. C., Sept. 1907."

B. First American edition. New York, 1907.

C. Holograph manuscript, epigraph, unpublished, and dedication, both in French. 1p. n.d.

D. First edition dramatic version. *The Secret Agent. Drama in Four Acts.* Canterbury, 1921. Wrappers. One of 52 copies privately printed for the author inscribed on front wrapper which serves as title page: "To Elbridge Adams from his friend Joseph Conrad."

E. Limited edition dramatic version. *The Secret Agent. A Drama in Three Acts.* London, 1923. Dust jacket. Number 793 of 1000 copies signed by the author. Privately printed for subscribers only. From the William B. Leeds Collection.

F. Responses, holograph and typed, from George Bernard Shaw, Graham Greene, J. B. Priestley and George Orwell to a questionnaire prepared by *Wiadomości*, a Polish literary weekly. The questionnaire dated 18 February 1949 concerns Conrad's place in English letters. All generally agree that Conrad's work is outstanding, that it will survive, and that he influenced many later writers, including Faulkner, Hemingway, Wolfe, and Fitzgerald.

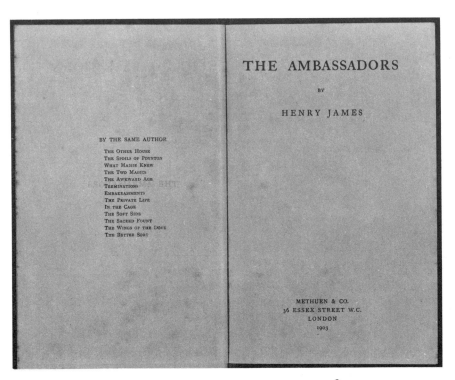

THE AMBASSADORS

BY

HENRY JAMES

BY THE SAME AUTHOR

THE OTHER HOUSE
THE SPOILS OF POYNTON
WHAT MAISIE KNEW
THE TWO MAGICS
THE AWKWARD AGE
TERMINATIONS
EMBARRASSMENTS
THE PRIVATE LIFE
IN THE CAGE
THE SOFT SIDE
THE SACRED FOUNT
THE WINGS OF THE DOVE
THE BETTER SORT

METHUEN & CO.
36 ESSEX STREET W.C.
LONDON
1903

16A FIRST EDITION

16. HENRY JAMES (1843–1916)

The Ambassadors (1903)

A. First edition. London, 1903.

B. First American edition. New York, 1903.

C. Limited edition. [New York], 1963.
Number 299 of 1500 copies signed by the illustrator, Leslie Saalburg. Made for the members of The Limited Editions Club by Irvin Silvers at the Garamond Press, Baltimore.

D. Holograph manuscripts with emendations, "The Objective Scene" and "Life as Art and Art as Life" by Stephen Spender. 55pp. n.d., two sections of *The Destructive Element, A Study of Modern Writers and Beliefs*. London, 1935. Spender comments at length on James' tendency to base his work on the impressions produced on him by families of ancient lineage, artistic tradition and wealth, and names *The Ambassadors*, a novel of Paris, as the most significant.

17. GEORGE MOORE (1852–1933)

Memoirs of My Dead Life (1906)

A. First edition. London, 1906.
Presentation copy inscribed: "To Edmund Gosse from his old friend George Moore June 15, 1906" with Edmund Gosse's bookplate. Laid in is an extra gathering, 16pp. with printed wrappers, containing a long passage omitted from the first edition.

B. Author's edition. New York, 1920. Dust jacket.
Number 673 of an edition of 1500 copies issued for private circulation. Laid in: prospectus with order form in which it is noted that it had always been Mr. Moore's desire to have printed a complete edition of the *Memoirs* in a text and format that he wished his readers to accept as a definitive edition. A fear of "Mrs. Grundy" caused the English publisher to leave out many interesting experiences from the first edition, and the American edition published in the same year sustained still further deletions. In this new edition the author has restored all the earlier matter eliminated from the English proofs and has completely revised and rearranged the text in the way he had originally intended it to appear.

C. Limited edition. London, 1921. Dust jacket.
Number 1 of 1000 copies signed by the author. Quarter vellum. From the library of Alfred A. and Blanche W. Knopf with "The Hovel" bookplate.

D. Proof sheets. London, 1921.
Numerous holograph emendations by the author and note at end: "Proof sheets of the new and final Edition of Memoirs revised and corrected by me. July 1921 George Moore." Jerome Kern bookplate.

E. Letters, two holograph and two typed, signed by Moore to David Garnett. Part of a long correspondence 1924–1931 in which Moore criticizes Garnett's work and offers suggestions for revisions.

F. Holograph manuscript, "George Moore" by Max Beerbohm with extensive revisions and numerous words and phrases blocked out. 16pp. with caricatures on versos of eight. n.d. Beerbohm describes Moore as a man who began with scant ability for expressing himself in writing but who, by making the most of what he had, earned for himself a gift not bestowed on him by Nature—the specific gift for writing. "Somehow," comments Beerbohm, "in the course of long years, he learned to express himself beautifully. I call that great."

18. J. M. SYNGE (1871–1909)

The Playboy of the Western World (1907)

A. First edition. Dublin, 1907.
Elizabeth Corbet Yeats' copy with her bookplate. Miss Yeats, sister of W. B. Yeats, founded the Dun Emer Press in Dublin in 1903 and published under that imprint until 1908 when the name was changed to the Cuala Press.
Large paper copy. Dublin, 1907.
Number 6 of 25 copies on handmade paper.

B. Advance copy. Dublin, 1907.
One of two advance copies bound up without the frontispiece before production of the play 26 January 1907, one for the use of the author, the other (this one) for the publisher, George Roberts. Roberts was an original member of the Irish National Theatre Society and for several years the secretary. He was, in effect, "publisher in ordinary" (under the imprint of Maunsel & Company) to the company and its successor, the Abbey Theatre.

C. Review copy. Dublin, 1907.
Broadside advertisement tipped in on front free endpaper. Laid in: review clippings and typed letter on publisher's letterhead referring to the controversy over the Abbey Theatre performance.

D. Second edition. Dublin, April 1907.
Sir John Martin-Harvey's copy with his bookplate. Sir John was one of the great actor manager-producers of his day. This copy, used for the London production, has his notes scattered throughout and is inscribed: "To Jack [Yeats] from the Gomme! Adelphi. June 8th, 1907."

E. Theatre edition. Vol. X of the Abbey Theatre Series. Dublin, 1907. A. E. Coppard's copy.

F. First American edition. Boston, 1911.

G. Three holograph letters signed by Synge to Maire O'Neill, his fiancee, sister of Sara Allgood and a leading actress of the Abbey Theatre group. In a letter dated only "Tuesday," he writes of going to the Maison to finish reading The Playboy. Saturday night he writes of Lebeau's delight with the play, and 26 May 1907 after the last performance: "It was withdrawn for political reasons I believe."

H. Holograph manuscript with emendations, "Notes on Playboy. Lecture on Synge" by Louis MacNeice delivered at Athens where MacNeice was head of the British Council 1950–51. 36pp. Loose in grey wrappers with title in blue pencil, "1950—Athens" in red pencil, signature and "(British Council, Athens—lectures)" in blue ink.

I. Holograph letter signed by Arthur Symons to Miss Allgood (Maire O'Neill) 12 June 1909 soon after Synge's death, in which Symons expresses his high regard for the genius that was Synge, his originality of invention, the perfection of his pure Irish style, and his characters, products of a strange and varying imagination. He concludes with the thought that all who mourn Synge must know that his name will survive death.

19. E. M. FORSTER (1879–1970)

The Longest Journey (1907)

A. First edition. Edinburgh and London, 1907.
Presentation copy inscribed: "A.R.A.[insworth] from E.M.F. 30/4/07."

B. Typed letter signed from Forster to Frederic Prokosch written from the Reform Club 13 September 1930 and marked "Personal." Forster wrote in reply to a question directed to him by Prokosch:

> "Yes — I am able to answer your question: I like *The Longest Journey* best of my novels, although I am aware of its numerous faults. I have come a little nearer in it than elsewhere towards saying what I should like to say."

C. Holograph letter initialed T.E.S. by T. E. Lawrence to David Garnett 16 February 1928. Lawrence comments on the work of a number of his contemporaries including George Moore, Proust, Paul Fort, Rimbaud, Verlaine, D. H. Lawrence, E. M. Forster and others. He thinks *The Longest Journey* the most significant of all Forster's work. To him it appears great—

> ". . . just great, without qualification. It hangs permanently in my memory, as if it was stuck there: it's like rolling on a fly-paper, which I've seen a hairy lap-dog do. E.M.F.'s stuff clings."

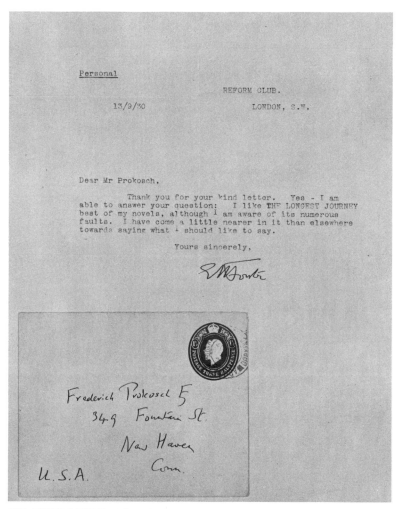

19B TYPED LETTER FROM FORSTER TO FREDERIC PROKOSCH

20. NORMAN DOUGLAS (1868–1952)

Siren Land (1911)

A. First edition. London and New York, 1911.
H. M. Tomlinson's copy with his signature on half-title.

B. New and revised edition. London, 1923.
Presentation copy inscribed: "To his Dear Reggie from Norman Douglas Florence. Nov. 1923 N.B. The Index was not perpetrated by myself."

C. Fifty holograph letters signed by Joseph Conrad to Douglas 1905–1913 bound in blue morocco. A long intimate correspondence in which Conrad often advises Douglas concerning his work. In a letter dated only "Saturday" he tells Douglas how to solve the difficulties he is having in getting *Siren Land* published, adding: "This matter must be settled now—next week. You'll feel happier and you'll be able to turn your mind to future work—to *production* instead of tinkering. See? This is my feeling." 2 June 1911 he writes of a visit from Cunninghame Graham "very full of admiration for Syren-Land and urging me enthusiastically to read it without loss of time. I said I would, at once, for the (about) 14th time."

D. Holograph notebook [1907–1920]. This general-purpose notebook contains notes on the everyday events in Douglas' life—a list of clothes to be taken on a trip: "2 shirts, 1 collar, 1 jersey, 1 pr. drawers, black pearl box"; a list, incomplete, of the contents of 9 boxes to be stored: stuffed and skinned birds, a marble bust of himself, mineral collection, reptiles in spirits, minerals and fossils, books, papers and addresses of numerous acquaintances, friends, and publishers, among them D. H. Lawrence, Jonathan Cape, Osbert Sitwell, Rebecca West, Mrs. Willard Connely and Grant Richards, to name but a few. Drawings and notes are tipped in on the last few pages.

NORMAN DOUGLAS BY DESMOND HARMSWORTH. OIL. 1933

21. D. H. LAWRENCE (1885–1930)

Sons and Lovers (1913)

A. First edition. London, 1913.
Presentation copy inscribed: "To my friend and protector in love and literature. Edward Garnett from the author."

Another copy inscribed to Garnett:
"And forgetting, startled, she looked for the hovering colour, & saw a rainbow forming itself. In one place it gleamed fiercely, and, her heart anguished with hope, she sought the shadow of iris where the bow should be. Steadily the colour gathered mysteriously, from nowhere, it took presence, there was a faint, vast rainbow. D. H. Lawrence."

B. First American edition. New York, 1913. Dust jacket.

C. Holograph manuscript, incomplete, with the author's extensive emendations, *Paul Morel* [*Sons and Lovers*], 271pp. n.d. Lawrence's pagination runs 1–353 with the following missing: 8–71, 93 (content continues from 92–94), 166, 335–352.

D. Page proofs, revised, including two unpublished sketches by the author. On the verso of one is a holograph note: "I hate this damned idea altogether—but I have no choice. The thing is to be in black & white. D.H.L."

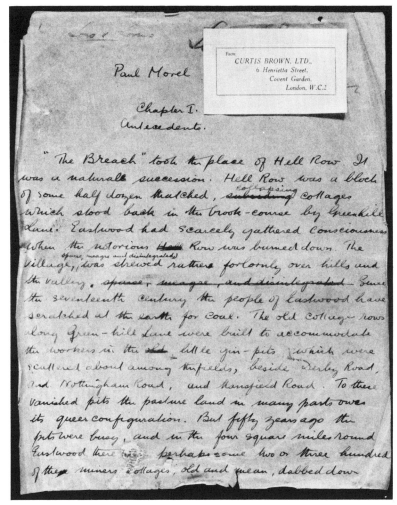

21C PAUL MOREL [SONS AND LOVERS]. HOLOGRAPH MANUSCRIPT
WITH AUTHOR'S EXTENSIVE CORRECTIONS AND
EMENDATIONS

E. Typed letter signed from W. Heinemann to Lawrence 1 July 1912 rejecting the manuscript of *Paul Morel.* Heinemann writes that he has read the manuscript

> "with a good deal of interest and, frankly, with a good deal of disappointment, especially after what you wrote to me with regard to your feeling about the book and the view you took that it was your best work."

In Heinemann's opinion the book is unsatisfactory because of its lack of unity and its want of reticence which "makes it unfit, I fear, altogether for publication in England as things are. The tyranny of the Libraries," he writes, "is such that a book far less outspoken would certainly be damned (and there is practically no market for fiction outside of them)." He continues:

> "In declining this manuscript, with many regrets, I would like to say that I am a great admirer of your writing, that certain parts in PAUL MOREL strike me as good as anything I have ever read of yours, but as a whole it seems to me painfully mistaken, if for no other reason than that one has no sympathy for any character in the book. A writer must create interest in his characters. Even, after a while, one's interest in Paul flags, — while, in the early part, the degradation of his mother, supposed to be of gentler birth, is almost inconceivable."

The letter concludes with Heinemann's statement that he should at all times be glad to read any of Lawrence's work and "it is a real disappointment to me to have to decline this book." Subsequently the manuscript was read and accepted by Edward Garnett, to whom the book is dedicated, for Duckworth & Company, London, where it was published in 1913.

F. Holograph letter signed from Lawrence to A. W. McLeod 2 December 1912. Writing after having completed *Sons and Lovers* and before beginning another work, Lawrence expresses his satisfaction—"It's quite a great work,"—but has doubts of its reception. Duckworth's advance payment of £100 on account elicits the comment: "I feel quite like a thief." Accompanied by a first edition inscribed: "To my friend A. W. McLeod from the author with affection and gratitude."

21F HOLOGRAPH LETTER FROM D. H. LAWRENCE
TO A. W. MCLEOD

22. GUILLAUME APOLLINAIRE
(1880–1918)

Alcools (1913)

A. First edition. Paris, 1913.
Original wrappers. Perforated "M.F." (Advance copy from the publishers.) Frontispiece: portrait of the author by Picasso.

B. Partial maquette by Maurice Darantière of poems from *Alcools* he had intended to publish in an edition illustrated with original etchings in color by Raoul Dufy. Proofs dated June 1930 with notations in the hand of Darantière, together with a dossier of about 30 documents relating to this edition which was finally abandoned after nearly 25 years of discussions. One of the documents is a four-page holograph letter written from London 25 August 1930 by Dufy, in which he gives specific details of his plans for the book to supplement information he has just written to André Malraux (then an editor for Gallimard).

C. Limited edition with original etchings by Élisabeth Gross. Paris, n.d. [ca. 1955].
Loose in sheets, original wrappers and slipcase as issued. In a typed letter dated 17 April 1953 Gaston Gallimard writes that although he had paid Dufy the full amount promised and he prodded him periodically over the years, Dufy had never given him the illustrations that would have enabled him to go ahead with the edition of *Alcools*. Darantière then commissioned Élisabeth Gross to do the job and this book was the result. The edition was limited to 110 numbered copies of which 10 carried an extra suite of the engravings. This copy, Number 1, was Darantière's, printed on Montval paper with two additional suites of the etchings on blue paper and three original drawings, one in gouache, one in wash, and one in charcoal.

D. Translation. *Alcools*. Garden City, New York, 1964. Dust jacket.
Put into English by William Meredith. Introduction and notes by Francis Steegmuller, who believes this to be an interesting and important work by a young poet breaking away from the past in search of freshness of expression and a new approach to reality, giving poetic significance where it had not been given before and renewing for modern man, bewildered by a rapidly changing world, "the beneficent shock of immediacy." Both Apollinaire and Steegmuller consider this to be the noblest function of the poet. Inscribed: "For Marion [Mrs. E. E.] Cummings, my little part of this. Francis Steegmuller. March '64."

E. Holograph letter signed by Apollinaire to F. S. Flint. 20 March 1914 thanking him for his review of *Alcools*.

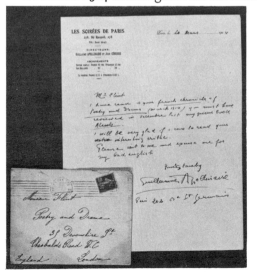

22E HOLOGRAPH LETTER FROM
APOLLINAIRE TO F. S. FLINT

23. MARCEL PROUST (1871–1922)

Du côté de chez Swann (1913)

A. First edition. Paris, 1913 (1914 on title page).
Presentation copy inscribed to Fernand Vandérem. Original wrappers. Half brown morocco sleeve and matching slip case.

B. Sixth edition. Paris, 1915.
Dated 1915 on front wrapper, but actually composed of the first edition sheets and title page with the 1914 date. Inscribed to Céleste Gineste, wife of Odilon Albaret, in memory and recognition of his deep affection for them both. Followed by an unpublished poem to Céleste, his young servant girl and wife of his chauffeur, whose first service to Proust was to tie the typescript of *Du côté de chez Swann* for mailing to his publisher in 1912; her last, ten years later, to take his dictation the final night of his life and hold his hand as death came.

C. Translation. *Swann's Way.* 2 volumes. New York, 1923.
Put into English by C. K. Scott Moncrieff. From the library of E. E. Cummings with his name and address embossed on the title page of both volumes.

English edition. 2 volumes. London, 1929.
The C. K. Scott Moncrieff translation. From the library of Harry and Caresse Crosby, founders of the Black Sun Press, with their sun insignia in pencil at upper right of front free endpaper volume 1.

Limited edition. New York, 1954.
C. K. Scott Moncrieff's translation with an introduc-tion by Justin O'Brien and illustrations by Bernard LaMotte. Number 299 of 1500 copies signed by the illustrator. In his introduction O'Brien points out Proust's reasoning on which he relied for eventual acceptance of his work: that when a new work appears, the public accepts from it, timidly, that which is least original and valuable—that which has been assimilated from an earlier art. As time passes more and more is accepted and gradually the new work creates its own posterity until there exists an ever-widening audience capable of understanding and loving it.

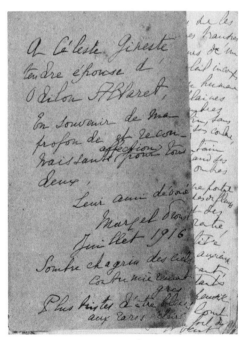

23B SIXTH EDITION INSCRIBED BY THE AUTHOR

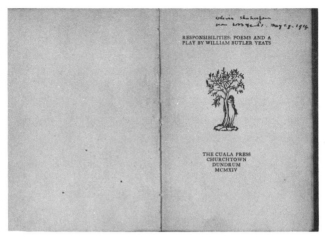

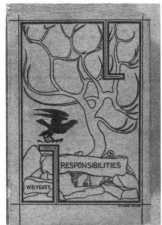

24A FIRST EDITION

24B ENLARGED EDITION

24D HOLOGRAPH LETTER

24. W. B. YEATS (1865–1939)

Responsibilities: Poems and a Play (1914)

A. First edition. Churchtown, Dundrum, 1914. Presentation copy inscribed: "Olivia Shakespear from W. B. Yeats. May 27, 1914." Number 10 of 400 copies.

B. Enlarged edition. *Responsibilities and Other Poems.* New York, 1916. Dust jacket.

C. Holograph manuscripts, (1) "On Those that Hated 'The Playboy of the Western World'" 1p. 1907; (2) "A Woman Homer Sung" 1p. n.d.; (3) *The Hour Glass*, new version with extensive emendations by the author, signed. 37pp. n.d. Accompanied by a printed copy of the old version with John Quinn's note on flyleaf: "1st printing before publication." n.d. The manuscript and pamphlet in separate silk protective jackets are in a crushed green levant morocco solander case. Listed in Quinn's sale catalogue as Item Number 11429.

D. Holograph letter dated only March 15 from a long correspondence between Yeats and Sturge Moore, some holograph, some typed, all signed, 1903–1937. Both sides of an important correspondence between two major literary figures of that time. In the letters written from various places, including Maud Gonne's home in Colleville, Calvados, and Lady Gregory's Coole Park, Yeats writes of his personal life, the past and the future, his hopes and expectations, but above all of his work. Always concerned for the beauty of his books, external as well as internal, Yeats makes suggestions to Moore for the covers which Moore so often designed. He inquires about a design for his new book, *Four Years 1887–91.* "Would a hawk do? Your hawk on the cover of 'responsibilities' is such a fine beast. I use the hawk as a symbol once or twice in the book."

25. THOMAS HARDY (1840–1928)

Satires of Circumstance (1914)

A. First edition. London, 1914.
Presentation copy inscribed: "To Lascelles Abercrombie from Thomas Hardy. December: 1914." Pasted on inside front cover is a newspaper clipping concerning Abercrombie's death, his service as one of Hardy's executors and his book titled *Thomas Hardy: A Critical Study*. London, 1912.

B. Holograph manuscript, "Thomas Hardy, T. S. Eliot," two lectures by Rex Warner, 23pp. n.d. According to Warner, Hardy's work is more closely related to that of the past English novelists—Fielding, Dickens, and Thackeray—than to the work of today's writers. Nevertheless, he is modern in the sense that he is disturbed —disturbed by life, "its ironies, its pity and its tragedy."

C. Holograph manuscript with emendations, untitled, by Dylan Thomas. 1p. Thomas expresses his approval of Hardy's work, particularly the poems and *Satires of Circumstance*, "tart, ungraceful, pitying cores of stories with knots at the end." Holograph note at bottom of page: "This nonsense from Dylan Thomas May 1950."

THOMAS HARDY BY REGINALD G. EVES. OIL. 1923

JAMES JOYCE BY JO DAVIDSON. BRONZE. 1929

26. JAMES JOYCE (1882–1941)

A Portrait of the Artist as a Young Man (1916)

A. First edition. New York, 1916.
Stephen Vincent Benét's copy with his signature and "March 1917" on flyleaf.

B. First English issue, American sheets. London, 1917.

C. *Stephen Hero.* London, 1948.
Printed for sale on the continent of Europe only. Edited with an introduction by Theodore Spencer. In reality a part of the first draft of *A Portrait of the Artist as a Young Man,* Spencer comments on the similarities as well as the differences between the two and notes particularly that Stephen as hero is an adolescent; Stephen as artist an adult. Original wrappers.
American edition. New York, 1944. Dust jacket.
Inscribed by Theodore Spencer, who edited the manuscript in the Harvard College Library and prepared this book: "To M. M. [Marion Morehouse] and E.E.C. [Edward Estlin Cummings] with love from T. Spencer. Feb. 1945." With Cummings' name and address embossed on front flyleaf and title page.

D. Typescript with typed and holograph revisions. "Portrait of the Artist" by Helen Joyce, Joyce's daughter-in-law. 14pp. n.d. Helen loved and admired her father-in-law and was concerned that no one really knew or understood him—that he was so often thought of only as the "mad genius" who wrote the jumbled and often incomprehensible words of *Finnegans Wake.* Here she presents Joyce as she knew him, a portrait of the artist in his middle years.

27. FORD MADOX FORD (1873–1939)

The Good Soldier (1915)

A. First edition. London, 1915.
Evelyn Waugh's copy with his bookplate.

B. First American edition. New York, 1915.

C. First appearance of the beginning of *The Good Soldier* under the title "The Saddest Story." *Blast* No. 1. June 20, 1914.

D. Later edition. New York, 1951. Dust jacket.
With a dedicatory letter to Stella Ford and an interpretation by Mark Schorer. Accompanied by an advance copy consisting of unbound sewn gatherings laid in dust jacket.

E. Typed letter signed by Ford to Rupert Croft-Cooke, dated only 2 November, with holograph note at top of page and following his signature: "I used to be Hueffer but changed my surname some time ago."

28. NORMAN DOUGLAS (1868–1952)

South Wind (1917)

A. First edition. London, 1917.
Presentation copy with holograph note on flyleaf to "Dear Tommy" in which Douglas complains that the publisher "boiled down" his fifty original chapters to forty "in order to save a page or two of paper (!)— destroying the structure of the book and its literary presentation" and lists the pages on which changes and corrections occur. The note signed "Norman" is dated 4 February 1944.

Another copy. Author's copy stamped "N.D." in purple on inside front cover. A few holograph corrections. Former arrangement of chapters on back free endpaper. The first two lines on page 335 transposed as described by Cecil Woolf in his bibliography.

Another copy. Dust jacket.
With the first two lines on page 335 in correct order.

27E TYPED LETTER WITH
HOLOGRAPH NOTE

28A FIRST EDITION

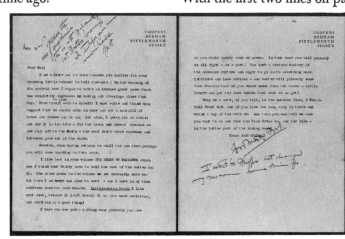

B. Page proofs. London, 1917.
Corrected by the author with holograph note on half-title: "First proofs. Corrected by me. Norman Douglas." Notes on back paste-down endpaper supply information as to state of proofs, corrections and additions. The poor quality of the paper makes it difficult to decipher corrections. Laid in between pages 444 and 445 is a portion of a proof page on paper of better quality with four lines circled in red ink and note: "This is the addition at bottom of page," referring to penciled notes on page 445 which are unreadable. Half brown morocco, decorated boards.

C. Limited signed issue. London, 1922.
Printed on light blue paper from the same setting as the original edition. Number 149 of 150 copies signed by the author. T. E. Lawrence's copy with initials "T.E.L." in upper right of front fly-leaf.

D. First American edition. New York, 1925.
Presentation copy inscribed: "To Fanny Hurst from Norman Douglas. 22 Nov. 1929. Not *nearly* nice enough for you!" Pasted on inside front cover is a small photograph of Douglas with holograph note: "Made for Fannie Hurst, Florence, Italy. Nov. 20, 1929. by Bob Davis."

E. First illustrated American edition. New York, 1928. Dust jacket.
Illustrations by Valenti Angelo. From the library of Peter Rempe.

F. Two of a series of letters, holograph and typed, signed by Douglas to Edward Titus, literary agent. Evidently in response to a query by Titus, Douglas writes 17 October 1927: "I certainly have first editions of many of my books, . . . but no *South Wind*." He indicates 15 October 1929 that he is ready to sell the sole and exclusive license to publish *South Wind* in book form in French for fifty pounds, saying: "It would give me great pleasure to see SOUTH WIND in French, but I fear its colloquialisms will prove a troublesome task to the translator."

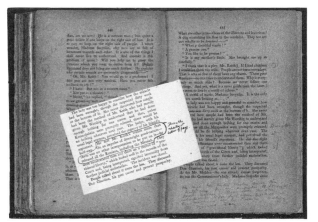

28B PAGE PROOFS WITH AUTHOR'S CORRECTIONS

28F HOLOGRAPH LETTER FROM DOUGLAS TO EDWARD TITUS

29. PERCY WYNDHAM LEWIS (1884–1957)

Tarr (1918)

A. First edition. New York, 1918.

B. First English edition. London, 1918.

Laid in: "Extracts from Press Notices of *Tarr*." *Nation* calls the work "beautiful and serious," reminding one of Dostoevsky because of its inquisitiveness regarding the soul, and because of its one figure of "vast moral significance." *Manchester Guardian* pronounces it "eccentric and formidable . . . a blow struck for seriousness in art and life." *English Review* considers it "baffling"; *New Witness,* "admirable . . . original"—an omen of a prose style to come, "hardly ever general, never diffuse, usually concentrated and penetrating," and calls Lewis a new writer taking definite and lasting leave of the romantic movement.

C. First revised edition. London, 1928. Dust jacket.

In a short preface to this revised edition published ten years after the first, Lewis speaks of *Tarr*, his first book, being, in a sense, the first book of an epoch in England. However, in turning back to it, he feels that the work should not appear again in its early form, having been written in haste during a time of illness and restless convalescence. Throughout this revised edition he has smoothed out that which was previously rough and given greater precision to the narrative, at the same time expanding a few scenes by the addition of new material.

D. Holograph manuscript, "A. J. A. Symons on Wyndham Lewis" with the author's revisions. 10pp. n.d. Symons, like others before him, pays homage to Lewis for breaking away from the old traditions and pointing the way to the novel of the future. He calls attention to *Tarr's* episodic plot, characters "described . . . in ruthless sentences that soar in fireworks of colloquialism" and a central figure "chiselled into reality almost before the reader's eye."

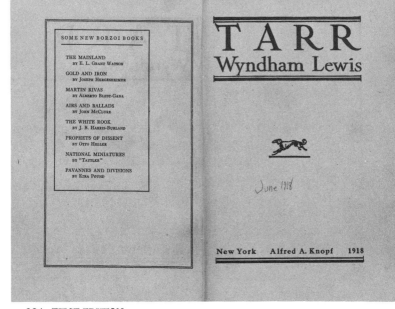

29A FIRST EDITION

30. T. S. ELIOT (1888–1965)

(a) *Prufrock and Other Observations* (1917)

A. First edition. London, 1917.

Review copy with publisher's notice laid in. Author's presentation copy inscribed to Frederic Prokosch with Eliot's note on half-title: "I have no doubt that this is the copy Rodker used. The two quotations, from Lucian & Virgil (pp. 35 and 39), are certainly in my hand." Another copy. Line drawn through author's name on title page and signed by Eliot while he and Mrs. Eliot were visiting at The University of Texas at Austin 23 April 1958.

B. Typed letter signed by Eliot to Robert H. Bagley 3 November 1952 on Faber and Faber letterhead. Eliot responds to an inquiry from Bagley concerning the possibility of making a film of *The Love Song of J. Alfred Prufrock*. He is flattered by Bagley's wish to make a film of the poem, but declines on the grounds that adapting his work to any other form than that originally intended tends to fix a particular set of imagery in people's minds in association with a poem. He prefers that the reader form his own images from the words. Furthermore, he writes: "the use of my own voice to accompany the pictures would give a kind of authenticity to one particular interpretation."

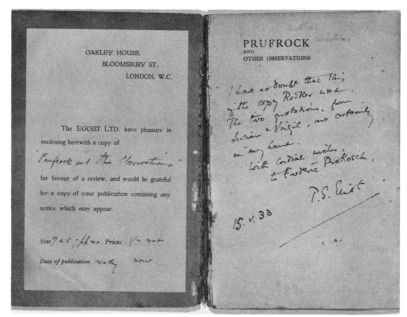

30A REVIEW COPY WITH AUTHOR'S INSCRIPTION AND PUBLISHER'S NOTICE

(b) *The Waste Land* (1922)

A. First edition. New York, 1922.
   Numbers 466 and 529 of 1000 copies. The "a" is missing from "water," line 138, page 22 of the first copies, but appears in later ones, while the "a" in "mountain," line 339, page 41, appears in the early copies and is missing in the later ones. Number 466 is in the flexible black binding of the early copies, Number 529 in the stiff black of the later ones.

B. First appearance. *The Criterion*. Vol. I. No. 1. London, October 1922.
   The two copies here are interesting not only because of the first publication of *The Waste Land*, but because of the comments of the publisher, Richard Cobden Sanderson, on the layout, binding and lettering of this first issue of his magazine.

C. First English edition. London, 1923.
   Presentation copy inscribed: "To Edith Sitwell with the humble and sincere compliments of T. S. Eliot. 3.iv.24." A few corrections in the text and notes.

D. Limited edition. London, 1961.
   Number 272 of 300 copies signed by the author. Printed in Dante type by Giovanni Mardersteig on the hand press of the Officina Bodoni in Verona. Quarter vellum, marbled boards and matching slip case, top edges gilt, others uncut. Evelyn Waugh's copy with his bookplate.

E. Holograph manuscript, *The Waste Land*. 23pp. [1960]. Fair copy made by Eliot for the 1960 London Library sale, distinguished particularly for the inclusion of a parenthetical line between lines 137 and 138 in "A Game of Chess."

   "And if it rains, a closed car at four
   And we shall play a game of chess
   (The ivory men make company between us)
   Pressing lidless eyes and waiting for a knock upon
                                                    the door."

F. Typed letter signed by Eliot to Richard Aldington 15 November 1922. A month after the first appearance of *The Waste Land* in *The Criterion*, Eliot writes to Aldington that it is now a thing of the past "so far as I am concerned and I am now feeling toward a new form and style."

G. Number 5 of 25 sets of illustrations for *The Waste Land* hand printed and hand lettered by Hugo Dreyfus from the original woodcuts by Emanuel Romano. New York, 1967.

31. PAUL VALÉRY (1871–1945)

(a) *La jeune parque* (1917)

A. First edition. Paris, 1917.
Number 144 of 575 copies on *Arches*. Original wrappers.

B. Limited illustrated edition. Paris, 1925.
Illustrations by Daragnès. Full parchment decorated with Daragnès's original pen-and-ink drawing of Valéry's serpent, original wrappers preserved. The artist's copy with his bookplate, three additional suites of the illustrations and presentation inscription (four-line poem) by Valéry. Tipped in is a holograph letter signed from Valéry to Daragnès concerning this edition.

C. Translation. *Words in the Mind.* London, 1965. Dust jacket.
Put into English by Charles Davy. Includes fragments of *La jeune parque* and Davy's examination of the total work of Valéry who is said to typify "an unresolved conflict between a scientific way of thinking and the symbolic power of poetry."

D. Thirteen holograph letters signed from Valéry to John Middleton Murry stemming from Murry's review of *La jeune parque* in the *Times*, the first dated 31 August 1917, the last 27 June 1936, with four not dated. Also one to Paul Souday 1 June 1922 in which Valéry thanks Souday, literary critic of *Le Temps*, for a review of his poems.

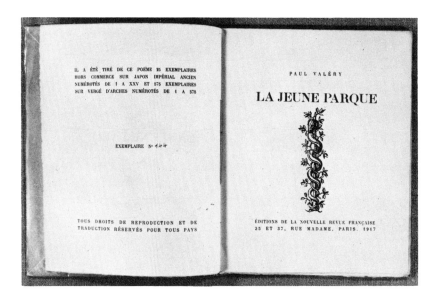

31A FIRST EDITION

31B LIMITED EDITION ILLUSTRATED
BY DARAGNÈS

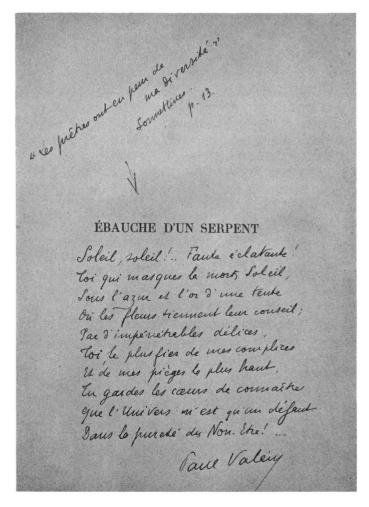

(b) *Charmes* (1922)

A. First edition. Paris, 1922.
   Number 1512 of 2000 copies on *vélin*. Quarter cloth, marbled boards, original wrappers preserved.

B. Second edition. First printing of two fragments of "Narcisse." Paris, 1926.
   One of 20 copies on *Japon teinte*. Original wrappers. Maurice Darantière's copy with his bookplate.

C. Holograph manuscript of a portion of "Ébauche d'un serpent" from *Charmes*, with holograph notation on detached half-title. Signed by Valéry.

D. *Poésies*. Paris, 1942.
   Number 1429 of 2000 copies on *heliona* in which portions of *La jeune parque* and *Charmes* are reprinted. Cream boards, original wrappers preserved.

E. *The Selected Writings*. New York, 1950.
   Edited by Anthony Bower and James Laughlin. Selections based on the Paris Morceaux Choisis volume chosen by Valéry himself and on previous translations. Bilingual text includes fragments from *La jeune parque* and *Charmes*.

31(b)C HOLOGRAPH MANUSCRIPT

32. GUILLAUME APOLLINAIRE (1880–1918)

Calligrammes (1918)

A. First edition. Paris, 1918.
Frontispiece: portrait of the author by Picasso. Original wrappers.
Another copy. Brown crushed levant with decorative pattern on front and back covers created by inlays in six colors of paper forming intersecting and overlapping letters which spell out the book's title, original wrappers preserved, top edges gilt, others uncut, slip case by Devauchelle. From the library of Carlton Lake.

B. Translation. *Selected Writings.* New York, [1948]. Dust jacket.
Bilingual text with translation and a comprehensive critical introduction by Roger Shattuck, who writes at length concerning Apollinaire's poetry, prose, drama and criticism. His verse, comments Shattuck, "hovers somewhere between lucidity and obscurity in a manner which can be satisfying when a careful balance is retained, or outrageously exasperating when it becomes lost to one tendency or the other." He calls Apollinaire "a magician in his poetry" and continues:
> "He wished to enchant the world. Inanimate objects make sounds; subtle emotions take the shape of animals and gods; men are drowned alive in oceans where life continues; and in their daily action ordinary people relive the fabulous deeds of legendary characters out of a distant past."

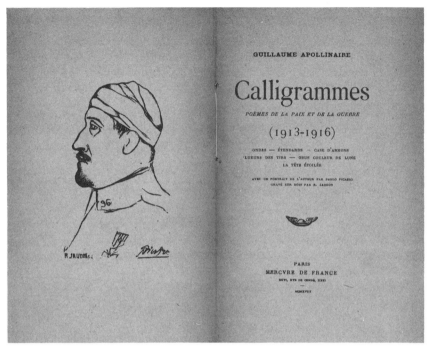

32A FIRST EDITION

33. GERARD MANLEY HOPKINS (1844–1889)

Poems (1918, posthumous)

A. First edition. London, 1918.
Edited with notes by Robert Bridges. A. E. Coppard's copy with his markings throughout and "A. E. Coppard . . . 1920 . . S.P. . . B. . H. . Ox." at upper left of inside front cover.

B. Page proofs. Bridges' notes lacking.

C. Enlarged third edition, fourth impression. London, 1952. Dust jacket.
Enlarged and edited with notes and a biographical introduction by W. H. Gardner. Edith Sitwell's copy with her notes on flyleaf and markings throughout.

D. Holograph manuscript, "In the Valley of the Elwy (Sprung and counterpointed)." 1p. 23 May 1877. On verso: "Spring (unfolding rhythm, with sprung leadings: no counterpoint)." May 1877. Also, holograph manuscript fragment initialed G.M.H. 1878, first published in *Poems* 1918 as verses 29 and 30 of "The Loss of the Eurydice."

E. Holograph letter from Gerard Manley Hopkins to Everard Hopkins dated 5 November 1885 at the beginning and 8 November 1885 at the end. In this long letter Hopkins writes of the difference between rhythm and metre—metre being a matter of arranging lines, rhythm one of arranging feet—and of the true nature of poetry, the "darling child of speech."

F. Typescript, "Gerard Manley Hopkins" by Edith Sitwell. 4pp. n.d. One of the poems which Miss Sitwell has marked in her copy of *Poems* is "The May Magnificat." In this essay she discusses Hopkins' style of writing, his use of colors that are at the same time "sharper, clearer, more piercing than those that are seen by the common eye," and points again to "The May Magnificat," citing it as an outstanding example of the poet's acute visual apprehension.

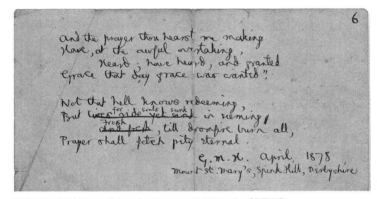

33D HOLOGRAPH MANUSCRIPT INITIALED BY HOPKINS

34. ARTHUR WALEY (1889–1966)

A Hundred and Seventy Chinese Poems (1918)

A. First edition. London, 1918.
   Errata slip tipped in.

B. First American edition, third printing. New York, 1920.
   Edgar Lee Masters' copy with his name on fly-leaf.
   Masters has checked some of the poems and turned
   down the upper right corners of pages for easy refer-
   ence.

C. Second edition, second impression. London, 1920.
   Signature of Alan Clutton-Brock, English journalist,
   critic and essayist, and "January MCMXXII" on front
   endpaper with a note that the book had been given
   by him to John Hayward. Laid in is a holograph letter
   signed by Waley to Hayward 26 October 1938.

D. *Translations from the Chinese.* New York, 1941.
   Ten water colors by Cyrus LeRoy Baldridge repro-
   duced in full color and forty-two brush drawings in
   gray, number nine on a special paper patterned after
   the old papers of the Orient. Frontispiece titled "Hata-
   men Street" signed by the artist. Most of these verses
   were previously published in *170 Chinese Poems.* In
   his preface Waley discusses the translation process for
   Chinese poetry, the poets he translates, and the subjects with which the poems deal. He concludes with
   an apology, explaining that it is difficult to understand
   "unfailingly" anything written a thousand or more
   years ago, but his Chinese friends have generally
   thought that his translations come quite close to the
   original—"closer, they have sometimes been kind
   enough to say, than those of any other translator."
   Vellum, red leather label with "Alfred A. Knopf" embossed in gold, red Chinese characters on spine, top
   edges gilt, gold moiré slip case.

E. Two holograph letters, the first dated only 13 October,
   the second not dated, both signed by Waley to Edith
   Sitwell to whom he dedicated *Chinese Poems,* 1946.
   In these letters Waley discusses translation of Chinese,
   particularly modern Chinese, and difficulties with the
   BBC concerning a "4 to 5 minutes talk on 'Chinese
   Civilization' or 'What China Stands For?'"

34E HOLOGRAPH LETTER FROM ARTHUR WALEY TO
EDITH SITWELL

35. E Z R A   P O U N D (b. 1885)

(a) *Lustra* (1916)

A. First edition, first impression. [London, 1916].
Number 4 of 200 copies with holograph note by Brigit
Patmore to whom the work was dedicated: "This book
was given to me by Ezra. It was dedicated to me under
the name Vail de Lencour, which is a nom-de-plume
Ezra chose for me." The circular stamp with the initials
"EP" designed by Edmund Dulac appears in pale
orange below the Patmore signature and on the title
page.

B. Page proofs. London, 1916.
With four poems not included in the first unabridged
edition. Author's note on first leaf.

C. First American edition. New York, 1917.
Number 1 of 60 copies initialed by Pound with a few
holograph corrections. Holograph note by Brigit Patmore on dedication leaf.

D. First American edition, second impression. New York,
1917. Dust jacket.

(b) *Hugh Selwyn Mauberley* (1920)

A. First edition. London, 1920.
Number 17 of 20 signed copies on vellum numbered
16 to 35. Presentation copy inscribed to T. S. Eliot:
"Thomas 'possom' or O possom, from the eminent in-
ventor, E.P. 1920."
Number 49 of 165 copies numbered 36 to 200. Quarter
tan cloth.

35(a)c FIRST AMERICAN EDITION

B. Typed note with doodles. n.d. Although unsigned, this
note concerning meter in poetry is easily identifiable
as Pound's.

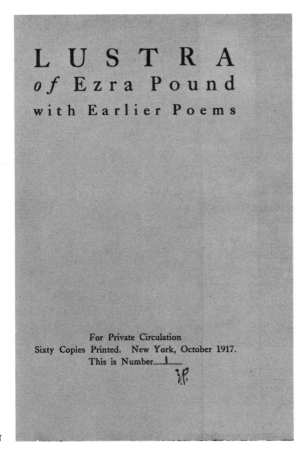

36. WILFRED OWEN (1893–1918)

Poems (1920, posthumous)

A. First edition. London, 1920.
Introduction by Siegfried Sassoon. Inscribed: "Autographed by Edith Sitwell who arranged the manuscripts for this publication."
Another copy. Dust jacket.

B. First American edition. New York, n.d. Dust jacket.

C. New edition. London, 1931. Dust jacket.
Including many pieces now first published and a memoir and notes by Edmund Blunden who admired Owen as a poet and valued him as a friend.

D. Holograph manuscript and typescript, "Wilfred Owen by Dylan Thomas" with the author's holograph corrections. 5pp. (4 holograph, 1 typed) n.d. In writing of this young poet Thomas illustrates the affinity between writers, the encouragement and recognition so generously given one to another when warranted. This is especially apparent in an incident narrated by Thomas as told him by Siegfried Sassoon. While confined to a convalescent home as a result of a war injury, Sassoon was visited by Owen. The two had never met, but Owen carried with him several copies of Sassoon's new book of poems, which he asked Sassoon to autograph. At the conclusion of the visit Owen gave the older man some of his poems and asked him if he would look at them and tell him if they were good.

"And Sassoon saw that they were good. And so did several other poets & men-of-letters to whom Sassoon sent them. And arrangements were made for a book of them to be published. Owen never saw that book."

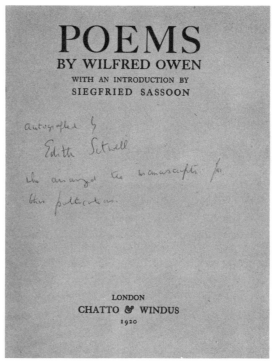

36A FIRST EDITION INSCRIBED BY EDITH SITWELL

37. LYTTON STRACHEY (1880–1932)

Eminent Victorians (1918)

A. First edition. London, 1918.
   Presentation copy inscribed: "Margot Asquith from Lytton Strachey. July 1918."
   Another presentation copy. From the library of Virginia Woolf inscribed: "Virginia from Lytton."

B. First American edition. New York, 1918.
   Edgar Lee Masters' copy with his markings throughout.

C. Five holograph letters signed by Lytton Strachey to Lady Ottoline Morrell 3 March 1918 to 16 June 1918 full of details concerning the publication of *Eminent Victorians* and its reception by the public. Strachey writes of his life passing
   ". . . almost entirely among proof sheets, which now flow in upon me daily. It is rather exciting, but also rather harrassing. All sorts of tiresome details and minor crises—about covers, illustrations, contracts, & so on—keep turning up: but my hope is that in about six weeks or so 'Eminent Victorians' will burst upon an astonished world."
   After publication he expresses nervousness because "the reviewers are so extraordinarily gushing, that I think something must be wrong." And still later: "The success of that book seems to be rolling on."

D. Typescript with holograph corrections and emendations, "Lytton Strachey" by R. A. Scott-James. 42pp. n.d. *Eminent Victorians*, published in the fourth year of World War I, met with varied reactions. Scott-James, commenting on its reception, notes that it delighted some and scandalized others. Some admired it for its subtle portraiture and deft handling of the theme, its irony and flexible prose. Others whole-heartedly approved of the attack against old idols already somewhat discredited but which, up until this time, no one had openly denounced.

38. D. H. LAWRENCE (1885–1930)

Sea and Sardinia (1921)

A. First edition. New York, 1921. Dust jacket.
   Eight illustrations in color by Jan Juta. Frieda's copy with "Brett" in pencil on front of dust jacket and front endpaper.

B. First English edition. London, 1923. Dust jacket.
   Eight illustrations in color by Jan Juta.

C. Typescript with holograph corrections by the author, *Diary of a Trip to Sardinia*, early draft of *Sea and Sardinia*. Wrappers, the whole fastened by one brad in upper left. 305pp. n.d.

D. First appearance of two chapters of *Sea and Sardinia*, "As Far as Palermo" and "Cagliari," in *Dial* October 1921 and November 1921.

E. Memorandum of agreement between Lawrence and Thomas Seltzer Inc. unsigned but with three holograph emendations on the first three of the four pages, initialed and dated: "D.H.L. 1 Sept 1921."

39. ALDOUS HUXLEY (1894–1963)

Crome Yellow (1921)

A. First edition. London, 1921.
Presentation copy inscribed: "Ralph Pinker his book Aldous Huxley."
Another copy. From the library of Harry and Caresse Crosby with the Crosby coat of arms stamped in gold on outside front cover, the Black Sun Press symbol on the back paste-down endpaper and two holograph notes in pencil on back free endpaper:
> "there is a suppressed chapter to this book called A Country Walk which appeared in a magazine called Coterie."
> "April third 1929 Met Huxley to-day—he was here for tea. Said he suppressed this chapter because it was poor not because it was erotic."

B. First American edition. New York, 1922.

C. Coterie. Autumn 1920.
Contains "A Country Walk," the suppressed chapter from Crome Yellow.

D. Holograph letter signed by Huxley to Lady Ottoline Morrell 3 December 1921 in which Huxley, somewhat angered and saddened by her charge concerning the characters in Crome Yellow, emphasizes the fact that they are merely marionettes "not only unlike anybody of my acquaintance, but also, deliberately & studiedly, unlike any whole & complete human being." He concludes his long letter:

> "This incident is to me another proof of something I said in the book: we are all parallel straight lines destined to meet only at infinity. Real understanding is an impossibility. I write something which seems to me immediately & obviously comprehensible for what it is. You, running on your parallel, read into it meanings I never so much as dreamt of. Others, on their parallels, find other meanings & contemptuous portraits of people unknown to you. What is one to do or say? I really don't know."

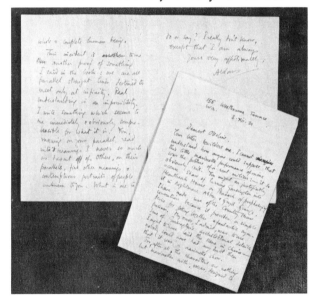

39D HOLOGRAPH LETTER FROM ALDOUS HUXLEY TO LADY OTTOLINE MORRELL

40. KATHERINE MANSFIELD (1888–1923)

The Garden Party (1922)

A. First edition. London, 1922.
Presentation copy inscribed: "To John Galsworthy in remembrance of his kindness Katherine Mansfield February 1922."

B. Limited edition. London, 1939.
Colored lithographs by Marie Laurencin. Number 23 of 1200 copies of which Numbers 1–30 are signed by the artist. Inscribed by Marie Laurencin to Lucy O'Brien. Publisher's note tipped in. Full crushed green levant.
Another copy. Number 181 of 1200 copies.

C. Two holograph letters signed by Miss Mansfield to Alfred A. Knopf, publisher. In the first, dated 20 January 1922, she apologizes for the delay in sending the corrected proofs to *The Garden Party* explaining that the London typist to whom she had sent the typescript to be duplicated only, took pity on her spelling and the bad grammar of the exiled children and made changes which were not discovered until she received the English proofs. A short note 18 March 1922 accompanies a few reviews: "It has been successful so far. I think it possible the tide has turned in favor of short stories. But perhaps thats the optimism of one who loves that form."

D. Long holograph letter signed by Katherine Mansfield to Lady Ottoline Morrell 4 March 1922 thanking her for a "beautiful letter" in which she expressed pleasure in *The Garden Party*, saying there had been reviews and a few notes from strangers but this is not the same as hearing from friends:
"I didn't expect to hear and yet my 'subconscious mind' has been intensely interested in whether there are any letters or not! Don't think its bad pride that makes me feel like that. Its the 'you feel that too? you know what I was trying to say' feeling which will be with me while life lasts."

E. Holograph manuscript incomplete with emendations, "Katherine Mansfield day by day" by Frieda Lawrence. 6pp. n.d. Frieda does not write about her friend as an author. She feels others are more qualified. Then, too, although the two were often together they did not "talk ideas," for their tastes differed, Miss Mansfield being an admirer of form and Frieda caring only for "what new substance a person had to give."

41. W. B. YEATS (1865–1939)

Later Poems (1922)

A. First edition. London, 1922.
   Presentation copy inscribed: "Olivia Shakespear from W B Yeats. Dec. 7, 1922."

B. First editions of the works from which *Later Poems* was compiled:
   The Wind Among the Reeds. London, 1899.
   Presentation copy inscribed: "To Maud Gonne from W B Yeats, April 24. 1899." Holograph manuscript, "The Song of Wandering Aengus." 2pp. 14 April 1916.
   The Shadowy Waters. London, 1900.
   Presentation copy inscribed: "Maud Gonne from W B Yeats Dec 19. 1900."
   In the Seven Woods. Churchtown, Dundrum, 1903.
   Presentation copy inscribed: "How shall we know the dancer from the dance. W B Yeats." With the Frederic Prokosch bookplate. Holograph manuscript, "Never give all the heart. . . ." 1p. 6 March 1904.
   The Green Helmet and Other Poems. Churchtown, Dundrum, 1910.
   Presentation copy inscribed: "Mrs Edmund Gosse from W. B. Yeats Dec. 1910," below which is written in pencil: "The corrections are in the poet's handwriting. E.G." Holograph letter from Elizabeth Yeats to Charles Elkin Mathews tipped in.
   Responsibilities: Poems and a Play. Churchtown, Dundrum, 1914.
   Arthur B. Spingarn's copy with his bookplate.

The Wild Swans at Coole. Churchtown, Dundrum, 1917.
Presentation copy inscribed: "Olivia Shakespeare [*sic*] from W B Yeats." Holograph manuscript with revisions. 2pp. October 1918.
Michael Robartes and the Dancer. Churchtown, Dundrum, 1920.
Presentation copy inscribed: "Olivia Shakespear from her friend W B Yeats. Feb 19 1920."

W. B. YEATS BY ALBERT POWER. BRONZE

42. JAMES JOYCE (1882–1941)

Ulysses (1922)

A. First edition. Paris, 1922.

Number 86 of 100 copies on Dutch handmade paper numbered 1 to 100. Presentation copy inscribed: "To Edith Rockefeller gratefully. James Joyce Paris 2 March 1922." Original blue wrappers.

Another copy. Printed on *Arches*, the paper used in copies numbered 101–250. Press copy of Maurice Darantière who printed *Ulysses* at his press in Dijon. In place of the regular blue wrappers it is bound in wrappers of grey Ingres paper with the title and author's name on the spine in Darantière's hand. The preliminaries and a number of signatures are lacking. Laid in is an account of the printing of *Ulysses* cut from *La Stampa* of Torino. This copy was shown in exhibitions of Darantiere's printing in France, Germany, Holland and Belgium.

Another copy. One of 750 on handmade paper. Presentation inscription from Joyce to Robert Sage, associate editor of *transition*. Tipped in: a page of holograph manuscript in Joyce's hand defining the term "epitritus" [epitrite], apparently with relation to certain Joycean coinages and illustrating other metrical arrangements; the labels from a bottle of *Chateauneuf du Pape* 1920; and a proof before letters of a photograph of Joyce by Berenice Abbott that appeared in *transition* No. 13 Summer 1928. Vellum.

B. Page proofs heavily corrected by the author. Bookplate of E. W. Titus. Signatures of James Joyce and Sylvia Beach.

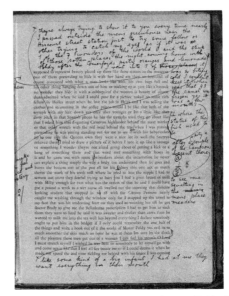

42B ULYSSES. PAGE PROOFS CORRECTED BY THE AUTHOR

C. Second Printing (for Egoist Press). Paris, 1922.
Number 1649 of 2000 copies. Eight pages of "Errata" laid in. Presentation copy inscribed: "To Jane Heep [*sic*] in token of gratitude. James Joyce. 7 June 1923. Paris." Miss Heap, associate editor of *The Little Review* from 1922–1929, wrote in "Lost: A Renaissance" for the final number May 1929 six years after Joyce inscribed this copy for her:

> "We have given space in *The Little Review* to 23 new systems of art (all now dead), representing 19 countries. In all of this we have not brought forward anything approaching a master-piece except the "Ulysses" of Mr. Joyce. "Ulysses" will have to be the master-piece of this time. But it is too personal, too tortured, too special a document to be a master-piece in the true sense of the word. It is an intense and elaborate expression of Mr Joyce's dislike of this time."

Five hundred copies of this edition sent to America were reported seized and burned by United States government authorities.

D. First American edition (unauthorized). [New York, 1929.]
Pirated edition of the ninth Shakespeare and Company *Ulysses* printed by Adolph and Rudolph Loewinger, New York, for Samuel Roth, publisher of *Two Worlds* and *Two Worlds Monthly*, and his brother Max Roth. Unauthorized by Joyce, it was sold illegally in the United States and numerous copies were seized by the Society for the Suppression of Vice 5 October 1929.

E. Protest against unauthorized publication of *Ulysses* in the United States. Paris, 2 February 1927.

F. *Two Worlds Monthly*. Edited by Samuel Roth. Volume 1 Numbers 1 through 4 1926–1927 containing the first four installments of *Ulysses* bound together. Bound in is Roth's "Prelude" 7 August 1927 relating his dealings with Ezra Pound which he alleges justified his publication of *Ulysses*. Number 85 of 500 sets for subscribers only.

Two Worlds Monthly Volume 3 Number 2 May–June 1927 with Roth's denunciation of Joyce's *Ulysses* and the slim Number 3 September 1927 issue in which he offers Joyce $2,500 to come to America to debate the issue of the alleged unauthorized publication.

G. Definitive edition. 2 volumes. Hamburg, 1932.
The final revised edition with typographical errors in previous editions corrected. Revised at the author's request by Stuart Gilbert. Gilbert's copy, one of ten on handmade paper printed for friends of Joyce, specially bound, signed by Joyce and with a holograph note by Gilbert.

Editorial copy for the first American edition. Original wrappers.

H. First authorized American edition. New York, 1934. With a foreword by Morris L. Ernst, attorney for the defense in the case against *Ulysses*, and the decision rendered by the United States District Court 6 December 1933. Presentation copy inscribed by the publisher: "For Morris Ernst. With deep appreciation Bennett Cerf. January 25, 1934. PUBLICATION DAY."

I. Limited edition. New York, 1935.
Introduction by Stuart Gilbert. Etchings and drawings by Henri Matisse. Number 1476 of 1500 copies signed by the artist, made for the members of the Limited Editions Club.

J. Six signed proofs of original etchings by Henri Matisse. New York, 1935.

K. First English edition printed in England. London, 1936.
Number 43 of 100 copies on mould-made paper bound in vellum, gilt stamped and signed by the author. Binding design by Eric Gill, top edges gilt, others uncut, decorated box. Laid in: "James Joyce, Bronze by Sava" and broadside describing the issue and carrying extracts from critiques by Stephen Spender, J. B. Priestley and E. M. Forster.

Number 813 of 900 copies on *Japon* vellum, green linen, top edges gilt, others uncut.

L. Trade issue. London, 1937.
Presentation copy inscribed: "To Morris Ernst, valiant and victorious defender of this book in America, in grateful recognition James Joyce Paris 5 October 1937." Accompanied by holograph letter signed by Joyce to Ernst 5 October 1937 thanking him for his "great service."

43. RAYMOND RADIGUET (1903–1923)

Le diable au corps (1923)

A. First edition. Paris, 1923.
Edition limited to 165 copies, this one unnumbered. Blue buckram.

B. Limited edition. Paris, 1926.
Lithographs by Maurice de Vlaminck. Number 25 of 25 copies on *Japon* with a set of the original lithographs on *chine* bound in. Half black morocco, original wrappers preserved, top edges gilt.

C. Translation. *The Devil in the Flesh.* London, 1949. Dust jacket.
Put into English by Kay Boyle. Introduction by Aldous Huxley which he concludes with commendations of Radiguet's work and "literary virtues,"—his directness, swiftness and simplicity.

D. Album formed by Maurice Martin du Gard, founder and editor of *Les Écrits Nouveaux* and *Les Nouvelles Littéraires*, relating to Raymond Radiguet's *Le diable au corps* and Jean Cocteau. Among the items are:

Original pen-and-ink sketch of Radiguet by Don, caricaturist for *Les Nouvelles Littéraires*, signed.

Holograph manuscript signed by Radiguet, "Mon premier roman," a discussion of *Le diable au corps*, its background and autobiographical aspect. 3pp. [1923].

Typescript signed of a publicity release concerning *Le diable au corps* prepared by the publisher Bernard Grasset, heavily corrected in ink by Cocteau. 2pp.

Proof of Grasset's publicity broadside for *Le diable au corps*.

44. RONALD FIRBANK (1886–1926)

The Flower Beneath the Foot (1923)

A. First edition. London, 1923.
Decoration by C. R. W. Nevinson on inside front cover. Frontispiece: portrait of Firbank by Augustus John. Portrait by Wyndham Lewis on title page.

B. First American edition. New York, 1924.
With the decoration by C. R. W. Nevinson in orange rather than blue as in the London edition substituted for the frontispiece portrait by Augustus John. Preface by the author in facsimile of his original holograph manuscript. Willard (Spud) Johnson's copy with "Spud" on front free endpaper.

C. Holograph manuscript with revisions, the author's preface to the American edition, 4pp. [1924], the fourth page being an alternate version of the first. Firbank relates here how the book "came about" from chance meetings with an American woman in Algiers, and his almost subconscious thought, "Her Dreaminess the Queen!" and later an Arab boy, "His Weariness the Prince!" asleep beside the summer sea.

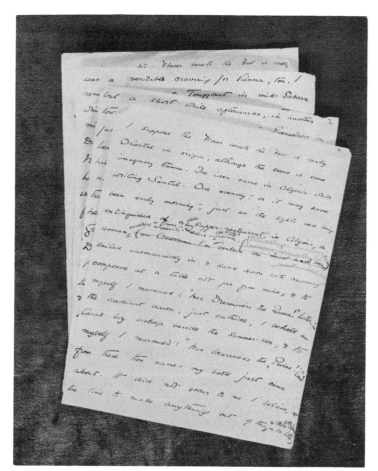

44C HOLOGRAPH MANUSCRIPT. PREFACE FOR
FIRST AMERICAN EDITION

45. E. M. FORSTER (1879–1970)

A Passage to India (1924)

A. First edition. London, 1924.
Presentation copy from the library of Virginia Woolf.
Inscribed: "Virginia from Morgan. 7–6–24."
Another copy. Dust jacket.

B. Large paper copy. London, 1924.
Number 129 of 200 copies signed by the author. Top
edges gilt, others uncut. From the E. DeGolyer Collection.

C. Holograph manuscript with emendations, signed.
520pp. n.d.

D. Holograph letter signed by Forster to Patric Dickin-
son 24 December 1960. Forster writes about *A Passage
to India*:
"I tried to keep the book as dateless as possible—
anyhow as regards wars: I was careful not to mention one, only to prophesy one—alas too accurately.
Part of it was written in 1913. The rest—with revisions—about 1923. It occurs as much in the early
20s as anywhere, of course with anachronisms."

E. Holograph manuscript, "Forster" by V. S. Pritchett,
with author's revisions. 4pp. n.d. Pritchett comments
on Forster's writing in general—his "startling power
of speaking in a natural private voice in public places,"
and calls *A Passage to India* a "grave and didactic
work . . . a comedy of the perils of understanding."

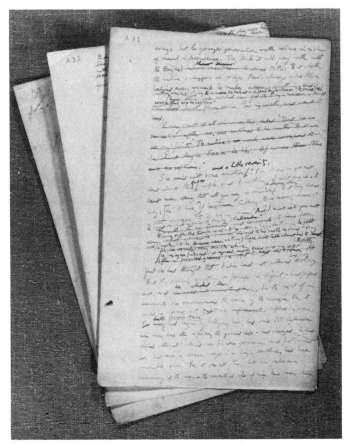

45C HOLOGRAPH MANUSCRIPT WITH AUTHOR'S CORRECTIONS

46. WALLACE STEVENS (1879–1955)

Harmonium (1923)

A. First edition. New York, 1923.
   From the library of Richard Church, English poet and critic.
   Another copy. Dust jacket.

B. Typescript, "Wallace Stevens, A Critical Study" by William York Tindall. 50pp. 21 May 1960. With extensive revisions throughout. Tindall points out that some may think it odd that an insurance man such as Stevens may also be a poet, and quotes Stevens' own words in justification: "It gives a man character as a poet to have daily contact with a job." As harmony and contrast exist together in the man so do they in most of his work, Tindall adds, but *Harmonium,* despite its title and "aural felicities," appeals more to the eye than to the ear.

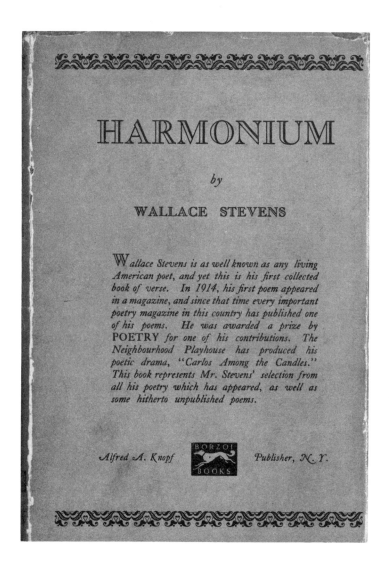

46A FIRST EDITION

47. E. E. CUMMINGS (1894–1962)

(a) *Tulips and Chimneys* (1923)

A. First edition. New York, 1923. Dust jacket.
Mrs. E. E. Cummings' copy with her initials "M.M."
[Marion Morehouse] and Cummings' signature on
front fly-leaf. Author's corrections on pages 14, 92 and
116.

B. Archetype edition. Mount Vernon, 1937.
With 73 poems not in the original edition. The colophon indicates that the edition was published in two
styles printed on Arnold unbleached all-rag paper, the
first 148 in a special binding. This copy is in St. Alban's
floral decorated paper over boards with navy polished
cloth back and fore-edges, unnumbered and unsigned.
Laid in is a holograph note 3 October 1964 by Lawrence Wallrich stating that this is the only copy bound
as specified for the deluxe binding—that it was never
published because the binder moved and all the sheets
were lost. Wallrich continues: "Authority is S. A.
Jacobs of course." Also, "Memorandum" from the
Golden Eagle Press.
Another copy. Number 206 of 481 remaining copies, inscribed by the author to his mother, Rebecca Haswell
Cummings: "for my indefatigable patroness R.H.C.
from the grateful author E.E.C. January 9 1938." Green
boards, vellum spine. Dust jacket.

C. Corrected galleys with holograph note on first page:
"please return this (by me corrected) set when you
send me the corrected equivalents EEC."

E. E. CUMMINGS SELF-PORTRAIT. OIL. 1938

(b) *Is 5* (1926)

A. First edition. New York, 1926. Dust jacket.

B. Typed letter dated only 21 December with typed signature from Hart Crane to Cummings recommending that he get a copy of *A Survey of Modernist Poetry* by Laura Riding and Robert Graves because "It has more gunpowder in it than any other book of contemporary criticism I've ever read—and as you (and Shakespeare) are the hero, you certainly shouldn't keep the cotton in your ears any longer."

48. F. SCOTT FITZGERALD (1896–1940)

The Great Gatsby (1925)

A. First edition. New York, 1925.
First issue with "sick in tired" on page 205.
Another copy. Scribner Press bindery office label inside front cover. Number 6220, 4–22–25. Bindery marks on preliminary pages.
Another copy. Later issue with "sick in tired" changed to "sickantired." Dust jacket.

B. Holograph letter signed from Fitzgerald to Joseph Hergesheimer. n.d. Fitzgerald thanks Hergesheimer for a letter he had written about *The Great Gatsby*.

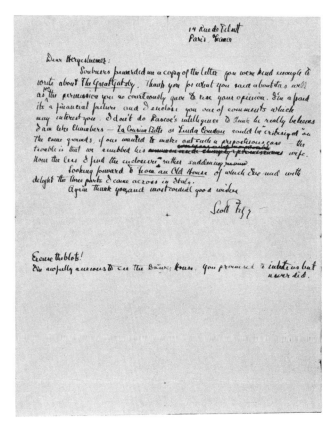

48B HOLOGRAPH LETTER FROM F. SCOTT FITZGERALD
    TO JOSEPH HERGESHEIMER

49. ERNEST HEMINGWAY (1899–1961)

In Our Time (1924)

A. First edition. Paris, 1924.
Number 70 of 170 copies on Rives hand-made paper. Presentation copy inscribed: "Ernest Hemingway, Artizan and writer, OK EH . . . Dorman-Smith to whom this is dedicated got to be a Lieut. Gen. I got to be a camp follower of the 4th Inf. Div. U.S.A."

B. First appearance of the first six chapters in *The Little Review* Exile's Number Spring 1923. Inscribed for Lee Samuels whom Hemingway described in a preface to *A Hemingway Check List* by Samuels as a man who "with no wish to profit from it, finds and collects all that you have written and then lost or forgotten. He not only finds them. He gives you copies of them for better or for worse. Finally they are to be given to a library. It is such a disinterested action that it is impressive to the point of being almost incredible in these times."

C. First American edition. New York, 1925. Dust jacket. Presentation copy inscribed: "To all the O'Neils with love from Ernest 1926."

D. Revised edition. New York, 1930. Dust jacket. Introduction by Edmund Wilson. Author's presentation copy inscribed: "To Mike Murphy Ernest Hemingway." Wilson comments on *In Our Time* as a key to Hemingway's later books. Their subject, he writes, is "suffering and making suffer, and their relation to the sensual enjoyment of life," but often the evenness and perfection of the prose tends to conceal underlying conflicts. Wilson rates Hemingway as "one of the most original of contemporary writers" catching in *In Our Time* the emotions of the American of 1917 and thereafter as no one before had done.

E. Reprint. Paris, 1932.
Presentation copy inscribed: "To Lee [Samuels] best always Ernest." Original wrappers. Accompanied by a revised American edition similar to that of 1930 but with 1931 on the title page, a mark-up copy used by Harry and Caresse Crosby in preparing the reprint, with changes and deletions marked throughout.

F. Typescript, carbon copy, "Big Two Hearted River," the last story in *In Our Time* with "Done Ernest Hemingway" in ink on verso of last page. 32pp. n.d.

50. E R N E S T   H E M I N G W A Y (1899–1961)

The Sun Also Rises (1926)

A. First edition. New York, 1926. Dust jacket.
With *In Our Times* for *In Our Time* on dust jacket and "stoppped" for "stopped" on page 181. Presentation copy inscribed to Lee Samuels.
Another presentation copy inscribed:
"To Frank J. Hogan Esq. wishing him much luck Ernest Hemingway. wrote first draft of this in 6 weeks in the summer of 1925—starting it on my birthday July 21 in Madrid and working on it there,

Valencia, Madrid again, St. Sebastian, Hendaye and finishing it Sept 6 in Paris. Rewrote it in Schruns in Vorarlberg Austria in Nov. and January. Made trips to U.S. in between."

B. First English edition titled *Fiesta*. London, 1927. Evelyn Waugh's copy with his bookplate.

C. Bantam edition. New York, 1949.
Original pictorial wrappers. Although inscribed: "For Lee [Samuels] this small tract against Promiscuity and anti-Semitism from which the word Jew has been deleted by the publishers Ernest March 6 1956," the word "Jew" appears once on page 2 and three times on page 196.

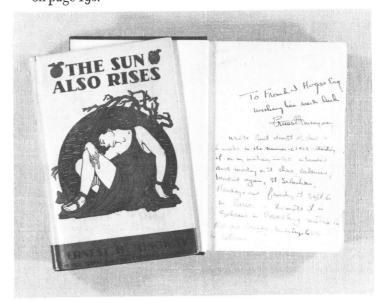

50A FIRST EDITION INSCRIBED BY THE AUTHOR

51. ANDRÉ GIDE (1869–1951)

Si le grain ne meurt (1924)

A. First regular edition. 3 volumes. Paris, 1924.
Number 50 of 550 copies. Original wrappers.

B. Special edition. Paris, 1939.
One of 5 copies on blue paper. Original wrappers.

C. Translation. *If It Die*. New York, 1935. Dust jacket.
Put into English by Dorothy Bussy. Number 842 of 1500 copies. Translated from the text of the first edition, Paris, 1920, of which only 12 copies were printed. Some of the proper names have been altered in accordance with the 1924, in reality the first public, edition. The omission of a short passage, also omitted from the 1924 edition because the author's cousins objected to it as inaccurate, is marked by asterisks. From the library of Alfred A. and Blanche W. Knopf.
Another copy. One of 100 copies on special paper signed by the author. Dorothy Bussy's copy, unnumbered, silk moiré on boards, top edges gilt, others uncut. Black board slip case.

D. Limited edition. London, 1950. Dust jacket.
Same text as the New York 1935 edition. Number 1462 of 1500 copies.

52. WILLIAM PLOMER (b. 1903)

Turbott Wolfe (1925)

A. First edition. London, 1925.
Presentation copy inscribed: "to Frederic Prokosch with compliments & thanks for compliments from William Plomer. London, 16 Nov: 1933." With the Prokosch bookplate. Laid in: small square of paper with Plomer's name and address, holograph (print), ink. Also laid in: blurb section of dust jacket with holograph corrections by the author and at bottom "P.T.O." where a holograph note concerning magazines to which Plomer contributed is discovered.
Another copy. Dust jacket. From the library of Virginia Woolf.

B. Reprint. London, 1965. Dust jacket.
With an introduction by Laurens van der Post. Author's presentation copy inscribed: "D. J. [Ackerley] with William's love. May, 1965."

C. Mimeograph copy, "William Plomer" by John Lehmann, signed, 14 October 1947. Prepared as a broadcast for the BBC series "Studies in English Letters." Lehmann discusses Plomer's debt to Forster as a teacher and places him among the most gifted of a generation of writers molded by Forster. "William Plomer has written novels, short stories, poems, biographies and critical essays; and in each of these mediums he has achieved something distinctly his own."

53. SOMERSET MAUGHAM (1874–1965)

The Casuarina Tree (1926)

A. First edition. London, 1926. Dust jacket.
   Presentation copy inscribed to his long-time friend and collector: "For Jerome Zipkin These stories were written after a first long visit to Singapore & the Malay States W. Somerset Maugham."

B. First American edition. New York, 1926. Dust jacket. From the collection of Klaus W. Jonas.

C. Mimeograph copy of "The Letter," one of the stories included in *The Casuarina Tree*, adapted for television by Felix Jackson. Draft No. 2 signed by Maugham. Holograph note: "Robert Montgomery Presents—Your Lucky Strike Theatre. NBC-TV 9:30 PM. EST Monday January 30, 1950."

D. Typescript with holograph emendations by the author, "The English Maupassant" by Desmond MacCarthy. 22pp. 4 March 1933. Man of the world as well as artist, Maugham, writes MacCarthy, "possesses all the gifts essential in a popular realist . . . and can tell a story as well as any man alive or dead." He cites several examples including "The Out-Station" in *The Casuarina Tree*.

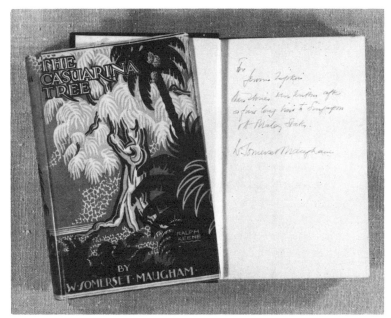

53A FIRST EDITION INSCRIBED BY THE AUTHOR

54. VIRGINIA WOOLF (1882–1941)

To the Lighthouse (1927)

A. First edition. London, 1927.

B. First American edition. New York, 1927. Dust jacket.

C. Typescript, carbon copy, "Virginia Woolf: A Tribute." by Stephen Spender. 3pp. n.d. Miss Woolf's best novels "or prose poems in the form of fiction," writes Spender, are "*The Voyage Out, Jacob's Room, Mrs. Dalloway, To The Lighthouse, Orlando,* and *The Waves.*" In each "she was 'trying to do something different,' especially with time. . . . A new way of writing a book was simply a new way of looking at life." He compares the quality of her writing with that achieved by a musician in exploring varying harmonies of an original theme, the original tune sometimes seeming lost while "depths far beyond the character of the original theme" are explored.

"The characters she creates . . . are well defined to be sure, but they are only the theme through which she explores quite other harmonies of time, death, poetry and a love which is more mysterious and less sensual than ordinary human love."

55. ANDRÉ BRETON (1896–1966)

Nadja (1928)

A. First edition. Paris, 1928.
Presentation copy inscribed to Gaston Gallimard. Original wrappers. Number H.C.*c.*
Review copy. Inscribed by Breton to Émile Vuillermoz.

B. Revised edition. Paris, 1963.
Original wrappers.

C. Translation. New York and London, 1960.
Put into English by Richard Howard. Forty-four illustrative plates.

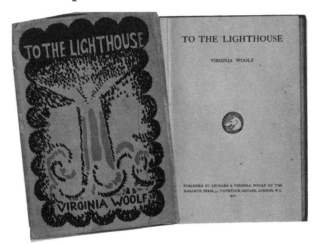

54A FIRST EDITION

65

56(a)D TYPED LETTER WITH HOLOGRAPH NOTES FROM
W. B. YEATS TO STURGE MOORE

56. W. B. YEATS (1865–1939)

(a) *The Tower* (1928)

A. First edition. London, 1928.
Presentation copy inscribed: "for Frederic Prokosch from W B Yeats 1928."

B. First American edition. New York, 1928. Dust jacket.

C. First appearance, *October Blast*. Dublin, 1927.
Presentation copy inscribed: "Iseult Stuart from W B Yeats Sept 1927." Connolly states that the collector will prefer *October Blast* to *The Tower* "even though its contents are somewhat slighter."

D. Typed letter signed with holograph notes at top and bottom from Yeats to Sturge Moore [21 September 1926] concerning a design for the cover of *The Tower* and enclosing a photograph of his tower, Thoor Bally-lee near Gorth, with the suggestion that the design should not be too unlike the real object, for "I like to think of that building as a permanent symbol of my work plainly visible to the passer by. As you know all my art theories depend upon just this—rooting of mythology in the earth."

(b) *The Winding Stair* (1929)

A. First edition. New York, 1929.
Number 53 of 642 copies signed by the author. Presentation copy inscribed on front endpaper: " 'an aimless joy is a pure joy' W B Yeats July 15, 1933."

66

Holograph note following statement of limitations: "One of four printed on green paper. J.R.W[ells]." Frederic Prokosch bookplate. Black cloth.

B. Paste-up for first edition inscribed: "J. R. Wells from W B Yeats July 1928." With Yeats' holograph corrections typed and tipped in and printer's notes throughout. Holograph note on half-sheet tablet paper and 3"x5" card with printing instructions tipped in.

C. Typescript with author's corrections, 28pp. n.d. Inscribed: "To Mr. Gaige [who] is about to put these poems into such a beautiful book W B Yeats." Accompanied by a typed letter signed by George [Mrs. W. B.] Yeats 13 March 1928 to Wells, the printer, saying she is sending the complete script of the book to be called *The Winding Stair* inscribed by Mr. Yeats to Mr. [Crosby] Gaige as requested.

D. Enlarged edition. *The Winding Stair and Other Poems*. London, 1933. Dust jacket.
Presentation copy "Inscribed for Lilian Davidson by W B Yeats, Nov 28 1935."

E. Proof. Review of *The Winding Stair* by W. B. Yeats by Richard Church. 1p. n.d. Church comments on Yeats' experimentation with technique and his personal reaction to recent volumes of Yeats' poetry, notably *The Tower*, which has made him think the unique continual development of this poet an intellectual one —that he neglected the dictates of his heart in favor of esoteric and occult interests. *The Winding Stair*, however, renewed his faith, for "In this new volume is all the man himself, in that same Satanic power which Milton, Blake and Shakespeare never ceased to exhibit."

F. Holograph draft of letter from John Masefield to Mrs. Yeats on the death of her husband 28 January 1939 expressing his and his wife's sympathy and his praise of Yeats, "the wisest & most beautiful mind among us." n.d.

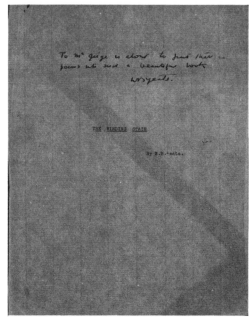

56(b)c TITLE PAGE OF TYPESCRIPT WITH YEATS' HOLOGRAPH NOTE

57. D. H. LAWRENCE (1885–1930)

Lady Chatterley's Lover (1928)

A. First edition. Florence, 1928.

Number 479 of 1000 copies signed by the author. Presentation copy inscribed: "to Edward Garnett who sowed the first seed of this book, years ago, at the Cearne—and may not like the full fruit. D.H.L." David Garnett's bookplate. Laid in: partial page from sale catalogue with holograph note by David Garnett: "This is the copy of *Lady Chatterley's Lover* borrowed and read by T. E. Lawrence."

One of two copies on blue handmade paper in full navy morocco. Limitation statement reads: "This edition is limited to One Thousand copies." It is signed by Lawrence, who has lined out "One Thousand copies" and substituted: "only two copies one for the master one for the dame none for the little boy that lives down the lane." Device of circle and arrow at upper left.

Second of two copies on blue handmade paper, brown boards similar to regular edition, signed by Lawrence who, as in the first copy, has lined through "One Thousand copies" and substituted: "only two copies and this is the dame's." Device of circle and cross at upper left. Pictorial cloth slip case.

B. Holograph manuscript with emendations, third version (first published) in two notebooks, the first paginated 1–408, the second 409–707, titled *My Lady's Keeper*

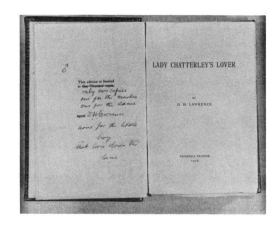

57A SPECIAL COPIES INSCRIBED BY THE AUTHOR

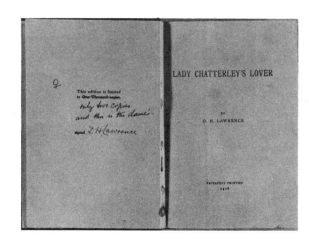

D. H. LAWRENCE BY JAN JUTA. CHARCOAL. UNDATED

with the author's signature and date "3 Dec. 1927." Label on second notebook indicates this version was privately printed in Florence in 1928.

C. Corrected typescript titled *John Thomas and Lady Jane.* "to Curtis Brown Ltd. 116 West 39th Street New York City. U.S.A." typed at lower left of title page. 423pp. n.d. Typed by Mrs. Aldous Huxley when Lawrence visited the Huxleys in Switzerland to try a change of altitude for his health. Lawrence had hoped that Curtis Brown would publish the work, but when no agreement was reached he proceeded with publication in Florence.

D. Popular edition. Paris, 1929.
The author's unabridged Popular Edition including *My Skirmish with Jolly Roger* "Written Especially and Exclusively as an Introduction to this Popular Edition." Privately printed. Original wrappers. Accompanied by a holograph letter signed by Lawrence to Lady Ottoline Morrell 3 April 1929 concerning his issuance of this cheap edition in an attempt to eliminate pirated editions which earn money for others and leave him with nothing. "I hope my own little overture will be a success. I have written a nice introduction telling them all what I think of them—one can't do more."

E. Holograph manuscript second version with the author's revisions in two notebooks, signed, the first paginated 1–265, the second 265–570. n.d. Label on the first notebook reads: "Second Version of L: Chatterley. Never been published in English."

F. First edition of first manuscript version. *The First Lady Chatterley.*" New York, 1944. Dust jacket.

G. Holograph manuscript, first version with the author's emendations in two notebooks bound together. 420pp. The work may be dated by Lawrence's note beside a stain on page 41: "Smudges made by John, the dog, near the stream behind San Polo Mosciano! 26 Oct 1926." Note on front cover: "Mm.S.S. [*sic*] of the first L. Chatterley. published By Dial Press in 1944."

H. First edition of second manuscript version *Le tre "Lady Chatterley."* Italy, 1954. Dust jacket.

I. *The Letters of D. H. Lawrence.* London, 1932. Edited and with an introduction by Aldous Huxley. Proof copy corrected by Huxley. Printed label on front wrapper, "REV. A. K. CHIGNELL Charterhouse Hull." Wrappers. Connolly suggests that the letters be read in conjunction with *Lady Chatterley's Lover.*

J. Two holograph letters signed by Lawrence to Lady Ottoline Morrell. He writes 28 December 1928: "You mustn't think I advocate perpetual sex . . . in and out of season. But I want, with *Lady C*, to make an *adjustment in consciousness* to the basic physical realities." Several months later, 5 July 1929, he writes of difficulties with Scotland Yard, of threats of criminal action, the holding up of his mail, and the confiscation of two copies of this book.

K. Three holograph letters signed by Lawrence to Edward Titus. Lawrence inquires about the progress of "Our Lady" 19 April 1929. A few months later 25 July he asks for a copy of "*Lady C.*" He is being asked to do a public expurgated edition but feels that this is a physical impossibility and wonders whether the first version could be printed. In a letter dated only "Wed." he writes: "I didn't see the review of *Lady C* in Nouvelles Litteraires—Could you send it me?—But I don't suppose it'll have any effect any more. The book is becoming, like Ulysses, an accepted fact."

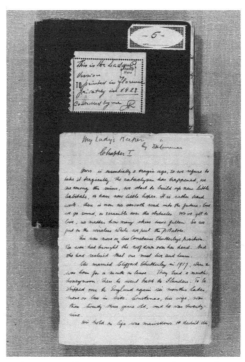

57B MY LADY'S KEEPER [LADY CHATTERLEY'S LOVER].
HOLOGRAPH MANUSCRIPT

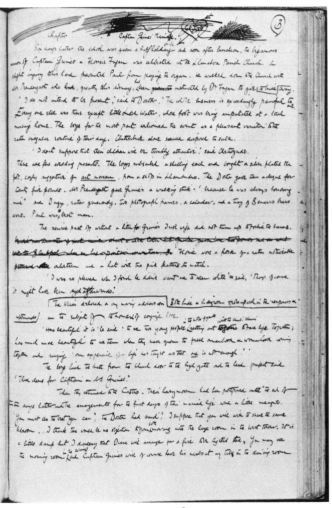

58. EVELYN WAUGH (1903–1966)

Decline and Fall (1928)

A. First edition. London, 1928. Dust jacket.
   Illustrated by the author.

B. First American edition. Garden City, New York, 1929.
   Illustrated by the author. Anthony Newnham's copy, a gift from William Doremus Paden, with his and Paden's bookplates. Mr. Newnham, who is preparing a bibliography of Waugh's works, has laid in a note on memo paper: "First American Edition with Doubleday, Doran's title-page. Later reissued with a cancel title-page bearing Farrar & Rinehart's imprint."

C. Special edition. London, 1937.
   Illustrated by the author. Number 1 of 12 copies printed for the author on rag mould-made paper and signed by him, none of which were for sale. Half red morocco. Waugh's copy with his bookplate. Also two proofs of the author's illustrations signed.

D. Holograph manuscript bound. 129pp. n.d. Numerous emendations by the author, some on verso. Quarter brown morocco with Waugh's bookplate.

E. Five loose pages from Waugh's extensive diaries in which *Decline and Fall* is mentioned several times:
   "October 4th, 1928. Immediately after breakfast, Chapman & Hall rang up to say that Doubleday & Doran wanted to take 'Decline & Fall' for America

and would give me $500 advance. The prospect seemed less brilliant later in the day when I discovered that by the time Brandt (?), Chapman & Hall and the American State had taken their share I shall get a little over half of the sum & that I shall not get it until the Spring of next year. Even so it is most agreeable news. . . .

"Monday . . . I see 'Decline & Fall' quoted as a best seller in one list. . . .

"Friday . . . Sales for the week of 'Decline & Fall' 157. Total 1093. When we touch two thousand I shall begin to feel more at ease about it. . . .

"Friday. Sale of 'Decline & Fall' 327 for the week. Second edition has 'gone to bed.' "

F. Typescript with holograph revisions. "Evelyn Waugh" by Cyril Connolly written for *Time* magazine. 7pp. 1951. PERSONALITY in upper left of first page. A holograph note by Connolly indicates that the paper was accepted and paid for but unpublished owing to the departure of the editor, T. S. Mathew. A second note reads: "Evelyn. Do send this back with suggestions & corrections & cuts. They wont use it till I have seen a proof." This typescript is especially interesting because of Waugh's self-image mirrored through his substitution of words, deletions of phrases—sometimes whole paragraphs—and the addition of new material.

59. HENRY GREEN (b. 1905)

Living (1929)

A. First edition. London, 1929.

B. Holograph letter 6 May 1929 signed by Henry Yorke [Green] to Edward Garnett in which he thanks Garnett for a review: "It was extremely kind of you to have written that appreciation of Living I have just seen in the Observer."

C. Typescript, carbon copy, "*For John Lehman's* [*sic*] *Talk*," n.d., in the opening sentences of which Green indicates very briefly one of his theories concerning the writing of a novel:

"I have long held that novels should be written as far as possible in dialogue only. The conventional approach by a novelist in which he presumes to know all about his characters, what they are feeling and thinking at any moment, seems to me as dead as the Dodo."

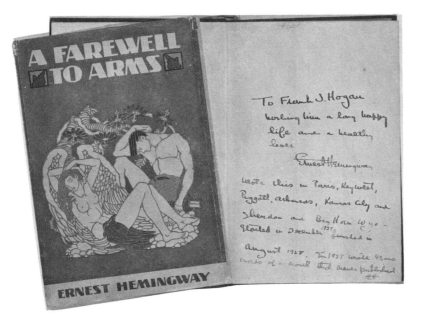

60A FIRST EDITION INSCRIBED BY THE AUTHOR

ERNEST HEMINGWAY BY ROBERT BERKS, BRONZE

73

60. ERNEST HEMINGWAY (1899–1961)

A *Farewell to Arms* (1929)

A. First edition. New York, 1929. Dust jacket.
   Presentation copy with Frank J. Hogan's bookplate, inscribed:

> "To Frank J. Hogan wishing him a long happy life and a healthy liver Ernest Hemingway. Wrote this in Paris, Key West, Piggott, Arkansas, Kansas City and Sheridan and Big Horn Wyo—Started in December 1927 finished in August 1928. In 1927 wrote 45,000 words of a novel that I never published E.H."

Second printing with author's note concerning characters and military organizations on page [10]. Dust jacket.

B. First appearance, *Scribner's Magazine*, May to October 1929. Four numbers signed by Hemingway, the last with a note in his hand: "summary not written by him."

C. Facsimile foundry proof. Number 57 of 93 copies of a privately printed note intended for the verso of a "bastard" title. Hemingway has underlined "bastard" and written in the right margin: "how Did they happen to use this word rather than illegitimate child?"

D. Limited edition. New York, 1929.
   Number 170 of 510 copies signed by the author. Presentation copy inscribed: "To Lee Samuels from his friend Ernest Hemingway." Decorated board slip case with red label.

E. First English edition. London, 1929. Dust jacket.

F. Illustrated edition. New York, 1948.
   Illustrations by Daniel Rasmusson. Introduction by Hemingway, Finca Vigia, San Francisco de Paula, Cuba, June 30, 1948. Signed by the author.

G. Holograph letter signed from Ernest Hemingway to David Garnett 10 December [1929] in which Hemingway expresses his admiration of Garnett's work and appreciation of Garnett's words of praise concerning *A Farewell to Arms*, although he finds them difficult to believe. He had written the book so many times trying to get it as he wanted it that it finally made no sense to him. He adds that should Garnett later wish to retract the praise, it will be all right with him.

61. ROBERT GRAVES (b. 1895)

Goodbye to All That (1929)

A. First edition. London, 1929. Dust jacket.

B. First edition, second issue. London, 1929. Dust jacket. Expurgated text with deletion of a paragraph on page 290 marked by 3 asterisks in a V-shape; deletion of a war poem by Sassoon marked by 3 asterisks in a V-shape at the bottom of page 341 and 4 in a diamond shape on pages 342 and 343. Erratum slip tipped in facing page 398.

C. Proof copy, uncorrected. London, 1929.
Accompanied by a holograph note signed by Simon Nowell-Smith to Graves 24 January 1964 requesting a manuscript to be sold in a fund drive for Oxford University. Graves' reply is appended to the bottom and verso of the letter:
> "This proof copy of *Goodbye to All That* is uncorrected but contains a page omitted from the published edition (at the instance of Edward Garnett) which I pasted in at the time. It also contains the Sassoon poem for which Sassoon made Jonathan Cape suppress the first impression—I hadn't asked his permission—and which I think is one of the most horrifying and truest poems he wrote in his best period.

> "I have also pasted in a poem (unpublished so far as I know) which I wrote in the Spring of 1919 ['Peace Day 1919']; the corrections seem to have been made some years later. . . . So far as I know this will be the only poem mss of mine that has been publicly auctioned."

Brown wrappers, quarter blue morocco case.

D. First American edition. New York, 1930.
Expurgated without the use of asterisks.

E. Typed letter signed by P. Beaumont Wadsworth, English journalist, to Graves requesting Graves' autograph in an expurgated first edition of *Goodbye to All That* and enclosing "10/– for your kindness." n.d. Graves' holograph reply is inserted in the left margin and at bottom: "How charmingly easy you make things—I needed that 10/– to pay the woman who washes up."

F. Holograph manuscript in the hand of Dylan Thomas, untitled, unsigned, 1p. numbered 10. n.d. Thomas describes Graves as a wit and an ironist, "a lyrical poet of great subtlety & skill" whose reactions to the world and his contemporaries, to the substance of poets and the poetical craft, are entirely peculiar to himself, a man whom "slogans of careerist literary propaganda never hoodwink . . . for a moment."

62. JEAN COCTEAU (1891–1963)

Les enfants terribles (1929)

A. First edition. Paris, 1929.
Number 6 of 31 copies on *Arches*. Original wrappers. Publisher's advertisement laid in. Mottled blue paper case.
Review copy. Inscribed by the author to Émile Vuillermoz. Original wrappers with publisher's protective glassine wrapper.

B. *Soixante dessins pour "Les enfants terribles."* Paris, 1935.
Paul Bowles' copy with "paul bowles Mexico juillet 1942" in ink on front endpaper.

C. Illustrated edition. Paris, 1950.
Illustrations by Nancy Gräffe. Number 263 of 150 copies on *Arches* numbered 151 to 300. Original wrappers.

D. Translation. *Children of the Game.* London, 1955.
Put into English by Rosamond Lehmann. Illustrations by Cocteau.

E. Holograph letter signed by Cocteau to unidentified recipients Christmas 1930 addressed to "Mes chers amis," evidently meant to accompany a copy of *Les enfants terribles*, asking the recipients to take it to Tisne or Brum after placing their corrections in their copy; Cocteau did not trust the disorder of the office.

F. Holograph manuscript incomplete, "Jean Cocteau" by Edith Sitwell. 4pp. n.d. Miss Sitwell stresses Cocteau's universality, profundity and intensity—his distinguished accomplishments as poet, dramatist, novelist, film-maker and writer on the arts. "Every subject he touches is seen by the reader for the first time, and by a strange light that would be blinding were it not the light of truth."

63. IVY COMPTON-BURNETT (1892–1969)

Brothers and Sisters (1929)

A. First edition. London, 1929. Dust jacket.

B. First American edition. New York, 1956. Dust jacket.
Laid in: "An Introduction to *Brothers and Sisters* a novel by Ivy Compton-Burnett" by Asa Benveniste who comments on the theme of her novels, the family, the confinement of several characters in a particular place from which there is no escape. She examines and exploits emotions under the resulting conditions of restraint. Although all Miss Compton-Burnett's novels present the same theme, she has succeeded in making each unique.

C. Holograph letter signed by Ivy Compton-Burnett to Rayner Heppenstall 2 February 1945: "It seems ungrateful not to comply with your suggestion, but I could not write dialogue between actual people. I have got too much into the way of doing what is really a very different thing."

64. HART CRANE (1899–1932)

The Bridge (1930)

A. First edition. Paris, 1930.
Number 48 of 50 copies on Japanese vellum signed by the author. Three photographs by Walker Evans. Original wrappers.
Review copy. One of 25 *hors commerce* from the library of E. E. Cummings with his name and address embossed on free front endpaper.

B. First American edition. New York, 1930. Dust jacket. Crane has lined through his name on the title page and signed it in ink, followed by: "January 3rd '31. damn wooly pens!" Laid in: newspaper clipping dated 28 April 1932 concerning Crane's death at sea.

C. Typescript, incomplete, 41pp. n.d. A few holograph corrections. "Indiana," "Quaker Hill," and all but the first page of "Atlantis" are missing. A second typescript of "The Dance" with Crane's holograph note to Allen [Tate] in upper left of first page indicating that it is a later and longer version. 2pp.

D. Corrected galleys with holograph note in ink: "Note! These galleys belong to me and are to be returned at once. Hart Crane." In pencil: "O.K. H.C." circled.

E. Production book. Composition book with holograph notes on 7 pages. Crane's name and address as well as those of Walker Evans inside front wrapper. Here is press information concerning the printing of the Paris edition and a list of individuals and publications to whom review copies are to be sent, including T. S. Eliot, D. H. Lawrence, Allen Tate, Jonathan Cape, *Times Book Review*, E. E. Cummings, Rebecca West, **and others.**

F. Typed letter signed by Crane to his mother 23 March 1926 four years before publication of *The Bridge*. "I'm back on The Bridge scaffolding again. Temporarily am Cristopher [*sic*] Columbus in mid-channel. The poem, as a whole, looks more exciting than ever to me."

64C TYPESCRIPT, INCOMPLETE WITH AUTHOR'S HOLOGRAPH CORRECTIONS

65. T. S. ELIOT (1888–1965)

Ash-Wednesday (1930)

A. First edition. New York and London, 1930.
"Out of series" copy from an edition limited to 600 copies. Signed by the author and inscribed to his first wife: "For Vivienne Haigh Eliot from her husband T. S. Eliot 15-iv-30."

B. First trade edition. London, 1930. Dust jacket. Presentation copy inscribed to Vivienne Haigh Eliot 9 November 1930.

C. First American trade edition. New York, 1930.

D. Two typed letters signed by Eliot to Rayner Heppenstall of the BBC 28 December 1950 and 7 February 1951 concerning the recording of Ash-Wednesday.

E. Typed letter signed by Eliot to Terence Tiller, also with the BBC, 21 May 1951. Eliot does not think he wants to record the whole poem in one day. He had rather make two or three appointments of an hour or so each "and take my time over it."

F. Production script with pre-recording schedule for transmission Saturday 29 December [1951] signed by Terence Tiller, Producer.

T. S. ELIOT BY SIR GERALD KELLY. OIL. 1965

66. EZRA POUND (b. 1885)

A Draft of XXX Cantos (1930)

A. First edition. *A Draft of XXX Cantos.* Paris, 1930.
Number 6 of 10 copies on Texas Mountain paper signed by the author. Original roan, all edges uncut. Nancy Cunard's copy with a photograph of Pound tipped in. Miss Cunard purchased the Three Mountains Press equipment in 1928, moved it to Chapelle-Réanville and rechristened it the Hours Press.

Another copy. Number 161 of 200 copies on Canson-Mongolfier paper with a portion of a photograph of Pound's "death mask," made about 1922 as a hoax, with a holograph note by Nancy Cunard tipped in at the beginning and a Pound-like typed "Note to Ez" inscribed to her by Bob Brown tipped in at the end. The Hours Press' copy.

B. First American edition. New York, [1933]. Dust jacket.

C. First English edition. London, 1933. Dust jacket.

D. Portions of *XXX Cantos* which appeared in book form before 1930:

A Draft of XVI Cantos. Paris, 1925.
Initials by Henry Strater. Number XI of XV copies on Whatman paper. White vellum stamped in gold.

Another copy. Number 52 of 70 copies on paper specially watermarked with a star, "Ezra Pound Cantos," and the device of the Three Mountains Press. Red parchment stamped in gold.

Author's proof. Some pages printed on special watermarked paper. "Author's proof" designated in print on the colophon page. Decorated wrappers.

A Draft of the Cantos 17 to 27. London, 1928.
Initials by Gladys Hynes. Number XI of XV numbered copies on Whatman paper. Green vellum stamped in gold.

Proof copy. "Criterion" in Eliot's hand at upper left of front wrapper. Although not marked as such, this is apparently a proof copy corrected by Eliot. The statement of limitations reads in part: "Six copies have been sent to various Libraries under the Copyright Act, and one copy to *The Times Literary Supplement* for review. This copy is number 13 printed for Olivia Shakespear." That portion referring to the review copy is lined out and a holograph note substituted: "No copies have gone out for review." Mrs. Shakespear's name is also lined out. Proofs of the red portions of Gladys Hynes' initials printed on separate tissue-overlays are laid in.

E. Typed letter signed by Pound to Milton Bronner 21 September 1915 in which he makes one of his earliest mentions of the yet unnamed cantos: "I am also at work on a cryselephantine [*sic*] poem of immeasurable length which will occupy me for the next four decades unless it becomes a bore." A decade and a half later in a letter typed on his letterhead, Rapallo [18 November 1930], he writes to Donal McKenzie:

"Afraid Cantos XXX costs ten bucks. One must live. If only 22 people want one to be printed they have to pay for the luxury. I spose there is an economic law of negative criticism. Convince enough people that an author is not worth reading and his work becomes difficult to obtain."

F. Typed letter signed by T. S. Eliot to a bookseller 16 July 1930 asking if he could get at two pounds a copy of the ordinary edition of Pound's *XXX Cantos* when it appears.

G. Typescript with holograph revisions by the author, review of Ezra Pound's The Cantos. *A Draft of XXX Cantos*, Paris: 1930 by Marianne Moore. 13pp. n.d. Miss Moore was one of the first to express approval:
"These Cantos are the epic of the farings of a literary mind. The ghost of Homer sings. His words have the sound of the sea and the cadence of actual speech. . . . The book is concerned with beauty. You must read it yourself; it has the surging of power that is mind and is music; it comes with the impact of centuries and with the impact of yesterday."

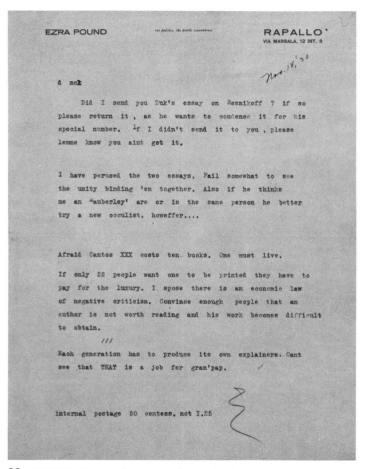

66E TYPED LETTER FROM EZRA POUND TO DONAL MCKENZIE

Preface

Gold Coast Customs   Edith Sitwell.

This poem is built on three ~~beds~~, levels, each ~~knowing the other~~ being a spiritual state reflecting the two others.

It has at the head this quotation: "In Ashantee a hundred years ago, the death of any rich or important person was followed by several days of national ceremonies, during which the utmost licence prevailed, and slaves and poor persons were killed that the bones of the deceased might be laved with human blood. These ceremonies were called Customs."

The poem was written in 1929, at a time when destitution was rife, and when a certain set of heartless fools, Gold Coasters, as one might call them, flaunted their riches at debased parties under the very eyes of those who had neither food nor shelter. It was of the spiritual death of these people, and the licence that prevailed in celebration of their death, that I wrote.

But the poem, too, has a more universal meaning than that. It speaks of the whole spiritual state that led up to the second World War. It was a definite prophecy of what would arise from such a state — what has arisen.

    "Do we smell and see
That ~~such~~ sick thick smoke from London burning?

67. EDITH SITWELL (1887–1964)

Collected Poems (1930)

A. First edition. London and Boston, 1930. Number 98 of 320 copies signed by the author. Errata slip tipped in facing page iv. Signature "E. R. S. Fifoot" on inside front cover.

B. First edition, trade issue. London, 1930.
One of 250 copies bound in crushed blue morocco. Errata slip tipped in facing page iv.
Another copy. Dust jacket. Errata slip tipped in facing page iv. Black cloth.

C. First editions of works from which selections were taken for *Collected Poems,* original manuscripts and related materials:
Façade. London, 1922.
First edition, "Façade" [Program] *Miss Edith Sitwell* on her *Sengerphone* with accompaniments, overture & interlude by *W. T. Walton.* Typed by Ainslie's Agency. Gray wrappers stapled. Issued for the first private performance at 2 Carlyle Square, Chelsea, London, 24 January 1922, as described by Miss Sitwell in the accompanying notebook. Typescript, incomplete, with holograph markings, of the concert version of the poems and the original score of Sir William Walton's Orchestral Suite for *Façade,* the score in pencil with some superimposing by the composer in a heavier

67C HOLOGRAPH MANUSCRIPT

pencil since it was used by him for conducting and became rather faint for easy reading. A few additions, mostly names of instruments, in the hand of Constant Lambert, who also conducted from this score.

Second edition. [First printed edition.] Kensington, 1922.

Number 49 of 150 copies signed by the author. Inscribed by Miss Sitwell to Mr. W. B. Wasbrough and later acquired by Richard Fifoot, the Sitwell bibliographer, whose signature "E. R. S. Fifoot" appears inside the front cover.

Typescript, incomplete, in which Miss Sitwell explains the poems in *Façade*: "*abstract* poems, . . . patterns in sound . . . virtuoso exercises in technique of an extreme difficulty. . . . Some of the poems have a violent exhilaration, others a veiled melancholy, a sadness masked by gaiety." 4pp. numbered 3–6. n.d.

Bucolic Comedies. London, 1923.
Errata slip tipped in facing page 6. Holograph manuscript in notebook with author's note on front: "Very Early Poems Some of which afterwards came in Bucolic Comedies Others have never been published." Extensive revisions.

The Sleeping Beauty. London, 1924. Dust jacket.
Presentation copy inscribed for the English poet and critic John Freeman "in admiration from Edith Sit-

well." Holograph manuscript with revisions in lined notebook with early title "The Sleeping Princess."
Troy Park. London, 1925. Dust jacket.

From the library of H. G. Wells. Holograph manuscript with revisions in lined notebook entitled "Colonel Fantoch The Navy Blue Ghost and other poems for Troy Park."

Elegy on Dead Fashion. London, 1926. Dust jacket.
Number 203 of 225 copies signed by the author, of which only 200 are for sale. Illustrations by Thomas Lowinsky. Presentation copy inscribed: "John Freeman from Edith Sitwell." Holograph manuscript with revisions in lined notebook entitled "First Workings at Elegy for Dead Fashion. First workings at Polka." Early title *Poor Young People*.

Gold Coast Customs. London, 1929. Dust jacket.
Inscribed: "Alyse [Gregory]—with love from Sylvia [Townsend Warner] and Valentine [Ackland]." Holograph manuscript with revisions in lined notebook entitled *Gold Coast Customs* on front cover. Label on back cover reads: "Workings at Gold Coast Customs (here called 'The Best Party' The Strawberry, and workings at a poem used eventually in 'Metamorphosis.'" Holograph manuscript signed with revisions entitled *"Preface Gold Coast Customs"* in which Miss Sitwell explains the structure—"three levels, each being a spiritual state reflecting the two others." 3pp.

68. ANTOINE DE SAINT-EXUPÉRY (1900–1944)

Vol de nuit (1931)

A. First edition. Paris, 1931.
   Preface by André Gide. Number 200 of 600 copies on *vélin*. Original wrappers.
   Review copy. Inscribed by the author to Émile Vuillermoz.

B. Translation. *Night Flight*. Paris, 1932.
   Put into English by Stuart Gilbert. Preface by Gide concluding:
   "I admire this work not only on its literary merits but for its value as a record of realities, and it is the unlikely combination of these two qualities which gives *Night Flight* its quite exceptional importance."
   Original wrappers.

69. WILLIAM FAULKNER (1897–1962)

Sanctuary (1931)

A. First edition. New York, 1931. Dust jacket.
   Presentation copy inscribed: "For Mr Alfred Knopf, with thanks William Faulkner New York 7 March 1931." With "The Hovel" bookplate.

B. First English edition. London, 1931. Dust jacket.

C. Galley proofs: (1) First version uncorrected; (2) corrected with extensive holograph and typed revisions; (3) killed matter—material omitted from final publication.

D. Typed letter from J. D. Salinger to Mrs. Elizabeth Murray 31 October 1941. Typed "Teddy" in lieu of signature. Salinger urges Mrs. Murray not to buy a copy of *Sanctuary*, for he would like to send her one. He dislikes the story but thinks the writing excellent.

68A FIRST EDITIONS
69A FIRST EDITION

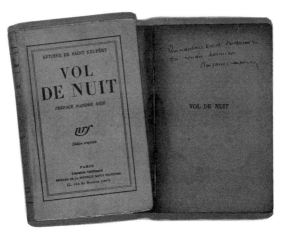

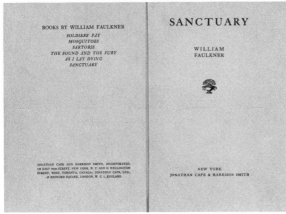

70. VIRGINIA WOOLF (1882–1941)

The Waves (1931)

A. First American edition. New York, 1931. Dust jacket. Willard (Spud) Johnson's copy with "Spud" on front free endpaper.

B. Two holograph letters signed by Virginia Woolf to John Lehmann. In the first, dated only Friday, she expresses pleasure that he is reading *The Waves* and asks his opinion "brutally & frankly," remarking that to her it seems a complete failure. Miss Woolf expresses gratitude 17 September [1931] for Lehmann's perceptive comments. She had "become firmly convinced that The Waves was a failure, in the sense that it wouldn't convey anything to anybody," and was dismayed to hear that 7,000 had been printed, "for I'm sure 3,000 will feed all appetites; & then the other 4 will sit round me like decaying corpses forever in the studio."

C. Holograph manuscript "Notes for a study of imaginative method in *The Waves*" by John Lehmann, with extensive interlinear revisions. 16 pp. n.d. Written after he had joined Hogarth Press in 1930/31.

71. EDMUND WILSON (b. 1895)

Axel's Castle (1931)

A. First edition. New York and London, 1931. Dust jacket.

B. Five holograph letters signed by Wilson to Edward Dahlberg March–November 1954 in which he writes of his travels in Europe, study of the Hebrew language and history, and the Dead Sea scrolls.

72. T. S. ELIOT (1888–1965)

Selected Essays 1917–1932 (1932)

A. First edition. London, 1932. Dust jacket. Presentation copy inscribed: "for Vivienne Haigh Eliot from T. S. Eliot 6.ix.32."

B. Limited issue. London, 1932. Number 114 of 115 copies signed by the author. Blue vellum, top edges gilt, others uncut.

C. First American edition. New York, 1932. Dust jacket. Advance copy. Publisher's slip tipped in.

D. A long series of letters 1930–1936 holograph and typed, signed from Eliot to Ronald Bottrall illustrates Eliot's concern for young poets and the critical assistance he so readily gave. Salutations progress from "Dear Sir" to "Dear Bottrall" to "Dear Ronald," indicating the growth of a personal friendship as well as a critical and business relationship. Eliot was editor of *The Criterion* during this time; many of the letters give evidence of the policies of the editorial board regarding publication of poetry.

73. W. H. AUDEN (b. 1907)

The Orators An English Study (1932)

A. First edition. London, 1932. Black cloth dust jacket. Presentation copy inscribed: "Joey with best wishes from Wystan Auden June 1932."

Another copy inscribed: "To John [Lehmann] from Stephen [Spender] Sellin, June 9th, 1932."

Another copy. Dust jacket.
From the library of Alfred A. and Blanche W. Knopf with "The Hovel" bookplate.

B. First American edition. New York, 1967. Dust jacket. Advance review copy. Publisher's slip tipped in. Foreword by the author in which he comments:
> "The central theme of *The Orators* seems to be Hero-worship, and we all know what that can lead to politically. My guess to-day is that my unconscious motive in writing it was therapeutic, to exorcise certain tendencies in myself by allowing them to run riot in phantasy."

C. Typed letter signed by Auden to unidentified recipient 8 November 1937 in which he gives two reasons based upon his own experience why poems sometimes fail. First, "the use of scientific terms which one has got from one's reading, but are not really part of one's normal tea-table experience," and secondly, "not visualising one's audience." His advice:
> "Try to think of each poem as a letter written to an intimate friend, not always the same friend. But this letter is going to be opened by the postal authorities, and if they do not understand anything, or find it difficult to wade through, then the poem fails. I used to try and concentrate the poem so much that there wasnt a word that wasnt essential. This leads to becoming boring and constipated."

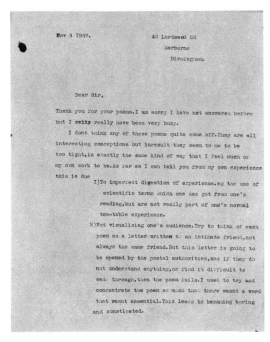

73C TYPED LETTER FROM W. H. AUDEN TO UNIDENTIFIED
RECIPIENT

74. LOUIS-FERDINAND CÉLINE (1894–1961)

Voyage au bout de la nuit (1932)

A. First edition. Paris, 1932.
    Presentation copy inscribed to Ludwig Lewisohn, German-born American novelist and critic. Half red morocco, marbled boards and endpapers, original wrappers preserved, top edges gilt.

B. Translation. *Journey to the End of the Night.* Boston, 1934. Dust jacket.
    Put into English by John H. P. Marks.

C. First illustrated edition. Paris, 1942.
    Fifteen drawings by Gen-Paul with original pen-and-ink wash drawing signed and dated " '39" laid in. Presentation copy inscribed by Gen-Paul to J.-G. Daragnès. One of 30 numbered copies on *vélin supérieur.* Original wrappers.

D. Two holograph letters from a long series signed by Céline to Milton Hindus, professor of English at Brandeis University and translator of Céline's works. Many of the letters written in 1947 and 1948 from Korsor, where Céline spent the greater part of his exile in Denmark under indictment for treason by the French government, relate directly to the composition of *Journey to the End of the Night* and *Death on the Installment Plan,* the characters, his literary aims and what he thinks to be the value of his own accomplishments.

74C ORIGINAL DRAWING BY GEN-PAUL

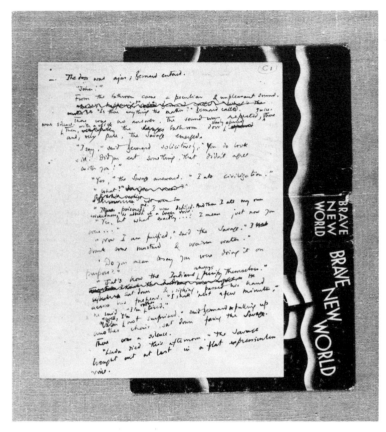

75E HOLOGRAPH REVISIONS

ALDOUS HUXLEY BY ALFRED WOLMARK. PEN AND INK. UNDATED

75. ALDOUS HUXLEY (1894–1963)

Brave New World (1932)

A. First edition, limited issue. London, 1932.
Number 247 of 324 copies signed by the author. Top edges gilt, others uncut. From the library of Alfred A. and Blanche W. Knopf with "The Hovel" bookplate.

B. Trade issue. London, 1932. Dust jacket.
Top edges stained blue, gilt lettering on spine.
Variant. Top edges not stained, black lettering on spine. Evelyn Waugh's copy with his bookplate.

C. First American edition, limited issue. Garden City, New York, 1932.
Number 218 of 250 copies signed by the author. Top edges gilt, others uncut.

D. Trade issue. Garden City, New York, 1932.

E. Typescript with extensive holograph revisions by the author. 260pp. n.d. Holograph title page with note by the author: "Corrected typescript—the nearest approach to a manuscript version." From the T. E. Hanley Collection.

F. Proof sheets corrected by the author. London, 1932.
Full brown morocco, top edges gilt, others uncut.

G. Reprint with a foreword by the author. New York, 1946. Dust jacket.
In his foreword Huxley reconsiders Brave New World and its validity in the present day, concluding that: "All things considered it looks as though Utopia were far closer to us than anyone, only fifteen years ago, could have imagined. Then, I projected it six hundred years into the future. Today it seems quite possible that the horror may be upon us within a single century. That is, if we refrain from blowing ourselves to smithereens in the interval."

H. Typescript, "Aldous Huxley. Who Wrote His First Novel in Complete Darkness" by unidentified author. 12pp. n.d. Holograph revisions, some by the author, others by Huxley. The importance of this typescript lies more in Huxley's revisions than in what the author has written. For example, to the question: "What do you think of reviewing in general?" Huxley's reply is quoted as: "Most of it is out and out journalism, of course." Huxley has underlined this and added: "Not very much. I have written too many reviews myself to be able to take most reviewing very seriously." "Dissatisfaction with one's work" replaces "the strain and agony of one's work." To the interviewer's comment: "But remarkably enough he came by none of the domineering moral bias which was one of the chief Arnoldian traits," Huxley added: "I'm really deeply preoccupied with ethical & religious themes." And, in reply to the question, "What do you think goes to the making of a writer?" to which the author gave Huxley's reply as "genius and vitality," Huxley struck out "genius" and substituted "talent."

76. NATHANAEL WEST (1902–1940)

Miss Lonelyhearts (1933)

A. First edition. New York, 1933. Dust jacket.
From the library of Alfred A. and Blanche W. Knopf with "The Hovel" bookplate.

B. First English edition. London, 1949. Dust jacket.
Introduction by Alan Ross who comments on the form and almost flawless structure of this novel, its compactness, penetration and poetic quality which makes it rank with the best that came out of America in the thirties.

77. ANDRÉ MALRAUX (b. 1901)

La condition humaine (1933)

A. First edition. Paris, 1933.
Number 55 of 150 copies on *vélin*. Original wrappers.

B. Limited edition. Paris, 1946.
Number 39 of 300 copies on *Arches*. Original wrappers. John Kobler's bookplate. Matching sleeve and slip case.

C. Translation. *Man's Fate*. New York, 1934.
Put into English by Haakon M. Chevalier who, in his introduction, calls attention to the fact that here, for perhaps the first time, is a writer in whom the revolutionary and the artist are one, justifying his place in society by dealing with matters that are important and helping to clarify human problems. He concludes: "Those of us who demand this can now point to *Man's Fate* and say: 'This is what we mean!'" From the library of Alfred A. and Blanche W. Knopf with "The Hovel" bookplate.

78. DYLAN THOMAS (1914–1953)

(a) 18 Poems (1934)

A. First edition. London, 1934.
Presentation copy inscribed: "With very much love from Dylan to Mother and Dad."

Another presentation copy. Inscribed to Stephen Spender with Stephen and Natasha Spender's bookplate.

Third presentation copy with grotesque drawings by the author on front and back endpapers, including an amusing self-caricature. Signature of Ruthven Todd beneath which Thomas has written: "From Dylan fondly '37." Mounted on endpaper facing the title page is the author's holograph manuscript of the 32-line poem commencing: "Do you not father me, nor the erected arm. . . ."

B. Original drawing. Self-caricature of the author sketched on dust jacket of *18 Poems*.

C. Second edition. London, [1942]. Dust jacket.
Variant. Green boards, cloth spine. Corrected by Thomas purportedly for *Collected Poems*. Numbers of poems have been lined out and titles substituted. Printing instructions on front of dust jacket.

D. Two letters of a long series 1937–1953 from Dylan Thomas to David Higham and members of the firm David Higham Associates who served as Thomas' agents from 1936 until his death and still administer his estate. Finance—Thomas' pleas for money to provide the temporary security which eluded him until his death in 1953—and the details of publishing are the dominant themes of these letters. The main prob-

78(a)B DYLAN THOMAS. SELF-CARICATURE. PENCIL

DYLAN THOMAS BY MICHAEL AYRTON. PENCIL. 1947

lem is pointed out in the first letter of the series typed and signed by Thomas 9 February 1937:

> "My capacity for even the simplest business undertaking is negligible; it sounds as though I'm trying to plead the notorious vagueness of the Dreamy Poet Type B classified by Punch, but really I'm a complete nitwit when it comes to replying to people, organising anything, making any sort of deal, keeping my tiny affairs in order. . . . And, before I forget, Simon and Schuster of New York say they are interested in my work. Do you think it advisable to get in touch with them about 25 Poems?"

In another, holograph, signed, to Laurence Pollinger 22 June 1940 Thomas urges him to attempt to persuade Dent's to republish *18 Poems* to which he would add *"ten recent—& unpublished,* except in magazines— poems, which should help the sale." Auden, he says, had done this with his republished first poems with very successful results. He writes of the original publication of *18 Poems:*

> ". . . published by the Parton Bookshop and the Sunday Referee. All this means is that the Sunday Referee, who were then running a weekly Poets' Corner or something silly like that, helped, a little, to finance the printing of the book. No contract was made, & the Referee, of course, took no royalties &, for that matter, no interest. The Parton Press no longer exists, & the copyright of the poems is mine."

E. Holograph manuscript with revisions beginning: "You wanted to know . . . why and how I first began to write poetry," which has become known as Thomas' "Poetic Manifesto." 9pp. n.d. The first draft, incomplete, also in holograph, consists of only 7 pages and bears a note at the top of the first page: "Notes Of, I Am Afraid, Little Help, for David In His Unenviable & Horrid Task of Writing About My Work."

(b) *Twenty-Five Poems* (1936)

A. First edition. London, 1936. Dust jacket.
Presentation copy inscribed: "To Wilfred very fondly from Dylan in God help us the Cafe Bloody Royal. 1937."
Another presentation copy inscribed to Ruthven Todd at the "Angel & Crown, '37," a public house frequented by both.

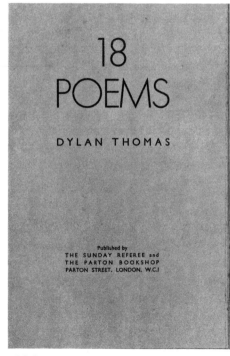

78(a)A FIRST EDITION INSCRIBED BY THE AUTHOR

79. F. SCOTT FITZGERALD (1896–1940)

Tender Is the Night (1934)

A. First edition. New York, 1934. Dust jacket.
Decorations by Edward Shenton.

B. Revised edition. New York, 1951. Dust jacket.
Edited and with a preface by Malcolm Cowley in which he states that this edition is based on changes made by Fitzgerald in his personal copy in which the pages are cut loose from the binding and rearranged and in which he has written: "This is the *final version* of the book as I would like it." A controversy still exists, however, concerning Fitzgerald's intent.

C. Paperback, third printing. New York, 1962.
A reprint of the first edition. Louis Zukofsky's copy with his critical notes throughout signed: "Louis Zukofsky, Polytechnic Inst. of Bklyn 3/21/63."

D. Newspaper clipping: "Scott Fitzgerald on Rewards," 8 August 1933. A letter from Fitzgerald to his 11 year old daughter "Pie" while she was at summer camp, briefly summarizing Fitzgerald's general beliefs and outlook on life: "All I believe in in life is the rewards for virtue (according to your talents) and the *punishments* for not fulfilling your duties, which are doubly costly." He advises his daughter to worry about courage, cleanliness, efficiency and horsemanship but not to worry about popular opinion, dolls, the past, the future, failure unless it comes through your own fault, mosquitos, flies, insects in general, parents, boys, disappointments or satisfactions.

80. HENRY JAMES (1843–1916)

The Art of the Novel (1934)

A. First edition. New York, 1934.
Introduction by Richard P. Blackmur. A. E. Coppard's copy with "A. E. COPPARD WALBERSWICK. CHRISTMAS 1935 from Armine" lettered by hand on inside front cover. Coppard sometimes emphasizes James' thought by underlining words or passages or questions with markings and comments in margins.

B. Five holograph letters from a long series signed by James to Hugh Walpole, many years his junior, dating from December 1908 to November 1915 which throw light upon James' later years, his continuing interest in young writers, and his happiness and satisfaction in knowing that he enjoyed "the sympathy of the gallant & intelligent young."

81. MARIANNE MOORE (b. 1887)

Selected Poems (1935)

A. First edition. New York, 1935. Dust jacket.
Introduction by T. S. Eliot in which he comments on Miss Moore's style and perception: "My conviction, for what it is worth, has remained unchanged for the last fourteen years: that Miss Moore's poems form part of the small body of durable poetry written in our time." Miss Moore has signed this copy and noted that it has not been corrected. Her note inside front cover, "See pps 29–31" directs the reader to "Nine Nectarines and Other Porcelain," where she has underlined words to indicate an unusual rhyme scheme.

B. First English edition. London, 1935.
Introduction by T. S. Eliot.

C. Galleys, with the poems corrected by Miss Moore, the introduction by Eliot.

D. Two letters signed by Miss Moore in which she writes of herself and her work. In a holograph letter 7 January 1949 to Mr. Griffith: "I do not feel that I am a poet, but that I am instinctively *attracted* to poetry." In a typed letter 6 July 1949 to Cid Corman, poet, founder and editor of *Origin:*

> "When I write, it is because I am entrapped by strong feeling or captured by an unanticipated felicity, so I do not write much. But however intensely felt, the product does not seem to me 'poetry.'"

She explains her style:

> ". . . a patterned [*sic*] arrangement with rhymes; stanza as it follows stanza being idential [*sic*] in number of syllables and rhyme-plan, with the first stanza. (Regarding the stanza as the unit, rather than the line, I sometimes divide a word at the end of a line, relying on a general straight-forwardness of treatment to counteract the mannered effect.) I have a liking for the long syllable followed by three or more short syllables. . . . I dislike the stock phrase and an easier use of words in verse than would be tolerated in prose. I feel that the form is the outward equivalent of a determining inner conviction and that the rhythm is the person."

E. Telegram from Wallace Stevens to Marianne Moore 29 January 1952: "I knock this morning at your door To bow and say Forever! Moore!" Accompanied by the envelope on which she has drafted a poem on the face in pencil and green ink and another on the verso in pencil.

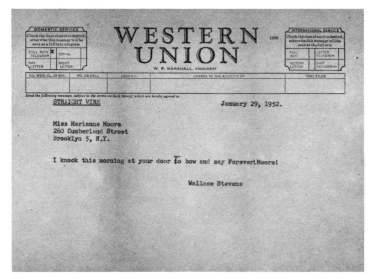

81E TELEGRAM FROM WALLACE STEVENS TO
MARIANNE MOORE

82. HENRI DE MONTHERLANT (b. 1896)

Les jeunes filles (1936–1939)

A. First edition. 4 volumes. Paris, 1936–1939.
   On *alfa*. Original wrappers. I. *Les jeunes filles*. 1936.
   Number 238 of 990 copies inscribed by the author to
   Frédéric Lefèvre. II. *Pitié pour les femmes*. 1936.
   Number 418 of 990 copies. III. *Le démon du bien*.
   1937. Number 122 of 990 copies. IV. *Les lépreuses*.
   1939. Number 260 of 350 copies, inscribed by the
   author to Marcel Thiébaut.

B. Reprint. 4 volumes. Paris, 1954.
   Number 140 of an edition of 1000. Decorated boards,
   tan board slip case. John Kobler's bookplate.

C. Translation. *The Girls*. New York and Evanston, 1968.
   Dust jacket.
   Translation by Terence Kilmartin. Introduction by
   Peter Quennell. Quennell discusses Montherlant's
   prose style—"uncommonly rich and various—tart,
   idiomatic, incisive, when he attacks some typical or
   controversial issue; measured, euphonious, poetic,
   when he deals with wider and less transitory themes,"
   and concludes:

   "*Les jeunes filles* may be read and enjoyed as a
   deliberately controversial book—an attack on 'the
   cult of Woman,' on the place that Woman has come
   to occupy in the modern European world; and as
   such it may have helped to break down many mas-
   culine taboos and phobias. But it is also an imagi-

native work of art, which, having absorbed and
digested its subject matter, presents us with something far more valuable and lasting. Circumstances
change; social problems vary; one day the unend-
ing War of the Sexes may be fought under completely different standards. But, so long as literature continues to play a part in our lives, Montherlant's story of *Les jeunes filles* is a book that will
retain its youthful freshness."

D. Holograph letter signed by Montherlant to F. S. Flint
   [16 November 1922] in which he uses Valéry's name
   to introduce himself to Flint and requests his opinion
   of his first work, *La relève du matin*.

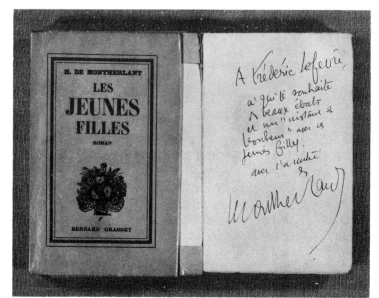

82A FIRST EDITION INSCRIBED BY THE AUTHOR

83. HENRI MICHAUX (b. 1899)

(a) *Voyage en Grande Garabagne* (1936)

A. First edition. Paris, 1936.
Number 47 of 1200 copies on *alfa*. Original wrappers.
Number 1310 of 110 copies *hors commerce* numbered 1201 to 1310. Original wrappers.

(b) *Au pays de la magie* (1941)

A. First edition. Paris, 1941.
Original wrappers.

B. Limited edition. London, 1946.
Number 202 of 500 copies. Inscribed: "E. E. Cummings, deferentially, from his publisher [Cyril Connolly] Christmas 1946 N.Y.C." with Cummings' name and address embossed on half-title. Original wrappers.

C. Translation. *Selected Writings.* New York, n.d. Dust jacket.
Put into English with an introduction by Richard Ellmann. Includes *Voyage en Grande Garabagne* and *Au pays de la magie*. In evaluating Michaux's work, Ellmann quotes the poet: "I do not know how to make poems, or regard myself as a poet, or find, particularly, poetry in my poems, and am not the first to say so." Ellmann calls this the quality of "insubordination" and based on it and the fact that Michaux wrote for himself, sometimes to "dispel tension," at other times for "an imaginary companion," or "deliberately to shake the congealed and established," Ellmann makes his final judgment:
> "Unawed by form or fashion in society or literature, he has waged his battle not against social or literary values, but, with a new tone and from a new perspective, against the tyranny of conventional experience."

D. Four letters, three holograph, one typed, signed from Michaux to Cid Corman, editor of *Origin*, 4 May 1955 to 21 December 1955.

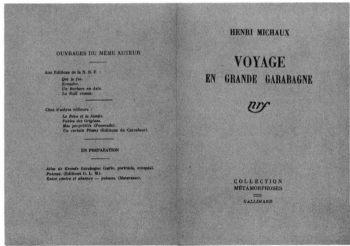

83(a)A FIRST EDITION

84. JEAN-PAUL SARTRE (b. 1905)

La nausée (1938)

A. First edition. Paris, 1938.
    Presentation copy inscribed to Paul Bowles. Tan cloth, original wrappers preserved.
    Another copy. Original wrappers.

B. Limited edition. Paris, 1938.
    Number 39 of 300 copies on *Arches* with a copy of the frontispiece on *papier de Chine* laid in. Original wrappers, matching sleeve and slip case.

C. Translation. *Nausea.* Norfolk, Connecticut, 1949. Dust jacket.
    Put into English by Lloyd Alexander.

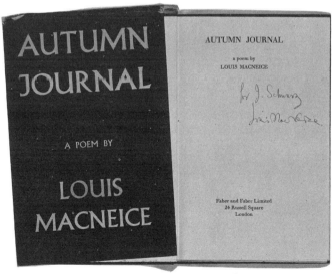

85A FIRST EDITION

85. LOUIS MACNEICE (1907–1963)

Autumn Journal (1939)

A. First edition. London, 1939. Dust jacket.

B. Proof copy. London, 1939. Wrappers.

C. American issue. New York, 1939.

D. Parts xiii and xvi, proof copy, with holograph notes in unidentified hand on first page of Part xiii: "His skit on the Classics Wit & Brilliance"; on first page of Part xvi: *"This on Irish Affairs* Shelly [*sic*] is right, The poet can (or should) be the great legislator, If only Ireland would listen to this poem."

E. Original holograph manuscript, "Poetry, the Public & the Critic," by MacNeice. 7pp. with 7pp. typescript bound in. 3 June 1949. MacNeice discusses the similarities between the spoken word and the lyric poem and points out that many poems become difficult because the poet must compensate for the motions and voice modulations used in speech. He then turns from this theme to take the reviewer [critic] to task for inconsistencies:
    "According to my reviewers . . . I am a surprisingly feminine, essentially masculine poet, whose gift is primarily lyrical & basically satirical, swayed by & immune to politics, with & without a religious sense, & I am technically slapdash & technically meticulous, with a predilection for flat & halting & lilting & Swinburnian rhythms, & I have a personal

& impersonal approach, with a remarkably wide & consistently narrow range, & I have developed a good deal & I have not developed at all."

He concludes by suggesting that the poetry reviewer would do well to put aside such generalities and discuss precise points—indicate to the reader where to look for the order of the poem and try to suggest the reason for this order—what the poet is getting at—for "It may very well be something that concerns the public too."

F. Holograph manuscript review of *Autumn Journal* by Stephen Spender signed with numerous revisions. 5pp. n.d. Spender expresses approval and disapproval of MacNeice: "Read his poems. They cannot be dismissed or explained away. They will give you a new and indescribable experience." He describes *Autumn Journal* as

> "a poetic journal kept from September to December 1938, . . . an autobiography, a confession, and, to some extent, pure journalism. . . . MacNeice's writing is something half way between a crooner's jazzy lilt and an Oxford drawl."

86. CHRISTOPHER ISHERWOOD (b. 1904)

Goodbye to Berlin (1939)

A. First edition. London, 1939. Dust jacket.

B. First appearance of four of the stories included in *Goodbye to Berlin*:

"The Nowaks." *New Writing* No. 1. London, Spring 1936. Edited by John Lehmann and signed by him on title page.

"A Berlin Diary." *New Writing* No. 3. London, Spring 1937. Edited by John Lehmann and signed by him on title page.

Sally Bowles. London, 1937. Dust jacket.

"The Landauers." *New Writing* No. 5. London. Spring 1938. Dust jacket. Edited by John Lehmann and signed by him on front free endpaper.

C. Five letters, four typed, one holograph, signed by Isherwood. From a long series to John Lehmann 1935–1945. Many concern publication in *New Writing* of the stories which make up *Goodbye to Berlin* and are filled with news of friends, some of whom are also writers, and comments on his own writing. He offers Lehmann 28 April [1936] five thousand words or so of *Berlin Diary* for Number 2: "It is only mildly (heter) dirty and chiefly about my landlady, fellow-lodgers, pupils etc." In another letter dated only May 8 he says:
> "One writes for an audience, and naturally, whatever happens, my audience is you all in England. Anything I have to explain I have to explain to you, and that puts me somehow on the defensive and inhibits me from writing. For there is really nothing to explain. . . . The language of "Goodbye to Berlin" is simply inadequate. I have got to invent a new way of writing, it comes back to that. And of course I hope I shall—"

87. JAMES JOYCE (1882–1941)

Finnegans Wake (1939)

A. First English edition. London, 1939. Dust jacket.

B. First American edition. New York, 1939. Dust jacket.

C. First limited edition. London and New York, 1939. Number 8 of 425 copies signed by the author.

D. Holograph letter signed by Joyce to Mr. [Daniel] Brody 5 March 1939 and advertising leaflet. "As regards *F.W* (no longer W.i.P.) I have just received some leaflets and send you one. In my opinion the price is altogether too high but it does not depend on me."

E. *Corrections of Misprints in Finnegans Wake.* New York, 1945.
For distribution free to purchasers of *Finnegans Wake.*

F. Holograph manuscript, "The Riverrun" for speaker and orchestra. 40pp. 1951. Words by James Joyce (*Finnegans Wake*), music by Humphrey Searle, with Searle's holograph note on front concerning its performance. From the T. E. Hanley Collection.

Connolly suggests that the best way to approach *Finnegans Wake* is through the *Anna Livia* recording and the *Tales Told of Shem and Shaun.*

G. First edition. New York, 1928. *Anna Livia Plurabelle.* One of a few special copies on green paper with black cloth binding for private distribution. Joyce received

JAMES JOYCE BY AUGUSTUS JOHN. PENCIL. UNDATED

four to be used for reviews in English periodicals. This is Cyril Connolly's copy with his holograph note on free front endpaper:

"Copy given to Cyril Connolly by Sylvia Beach— names of rivers supplied by J. J. while C. C. was preparing his essay 'The Position of Joyce' (Life & Letters. 1929)."

The last ten pages have considerable notes about the rivers supplied by Joyce while Connolly was in Paris at the author's home. Boxed with a copy of *Life and Letters* April 1929 with holograph note on page 273: "This article on Joyce largely supplied with his help! See copy of *Anna Livia*. Cyril Connolly 1960." From the T. E. Hanley Collection.

Number 294 of 800 copies signed by the author. Accompanied by a holograph letter from Sylvia Beach to Sisley Huddleston 2 November 1928. Miss Beach writes of the publication of *Anna Livia Plurabelle* and the scarcity of review copies. She suggests that since Huddleston had been the first to review *Ulysses*, Joyce might be pleased if he would do the same for *Anna Livia* and would be happy to lend his copy for that purpose. Since other Huddleston books at Austin bear either a presentation inscription or Huddleston's bookplate and this copy has neither, it may be the copy lent by Joyce. From the Carlton Lake Collection.

First English Publication, in *Criterion Miscellany*— No. 15. London, 1930.

Laid in: notice from the publishers concerning publication of *The Criterion*, a quarterly review edited by T. S. Eliot, with subscription form on verso.

Anna Livia Plurabelle translated into basic English. Orthological Institute, Cambridge England, 1929. Recording by Joyce boxed with three issues of *Psyche*, each containing an article about the translation.

First edition. Paris, 1929. *Tales Told of Shem and Shawn.*

Number 96 of 100 copies on Japanese vellum signed by the author. Green suede case.

One of 50 copies *hors commerce* in gilt case. From the library of E. E. Cummings with Cummings' name and address embossed on title page. Tipped in is a card from The Black Sun Press with a note to Cummings from Caresse Crosby: "We still hope to do your 'Puella Mea' if you will say 'yes'—We are now doing Hart Crane's 'The Bridge.' C C. 9 Sept 1929."

Corrected galleys signed twice by Joyce with a proof of the abstract "Earwig" portrait of Joyce as the internal ear by Brancusi. These proofs were formerly the property of Harry Crosby and are enclosed in a full green morocco case with the "Earwig" embossed in gold on front cover.

88. GRAHAM GREENE (b. 1904)

The Power and the Glory (1940)

A. First edition. London, 1940. Dust jacket.
   Presentation copy inscribed: "With love from Graham. March, 1940."

B. Holograph manuscript signed with extensive emendations by the author. 137pp. n.d. Note on title page: *The Power & the Glory*. Complete M.S. Note—please alter name Carol to Coral. Ch. 3 & after."

C. Typescript, "Graham Greene" by John Lehmann signed 30 September 1947. 5pp. Although prepared for "Studies in English Letters," a series of half-hour programs presented by the British Broadcasting Company, the notation "Not as Broadcast" appears at upper left, and it has not been mimeographed as have other essays in this series. In it Lehmann writes of Greene as "a master of the high-speed thriller" but whose "thrillers" comprise much more than the answer to who murdered the corpse in the locked bedroom or who stole the secret bomber plans. . . . Greene is interested in the psychology of the outcast from normal life and his stories, particularly *The Power and the Glory*, are inlaid with symbolism which gives them complexity and depth—"the depth of a poem." Lehmann calls this work a major achievement both intellectually and artistically.

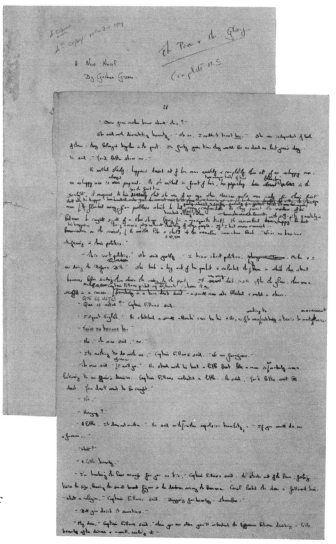

88B HOLOGRAPH MANUSCRIPT

DARKNESS AT NOON. Arthur Koestler. (Translated by Daphne Hardy)

In describing this powerful story I shall begin with poor tactics. I shall say that it might be considered an essay on political psychology based on a famous quotation from Machiavelli which is reprinted as a motto. I shall say that it is required reading for anyone who may have wondered about the notorious Moscow Trials, and gives us the first intelligible comment on the pragmatic reasons behind them. And then, lest this discourage anyone, I hasten to say that it is brilliant reading and anyone who has an adequate chair and a good lamp will not rise until he finishes it. I know I didn't and other members of our committee said the same. Even the good lamp will become an offense in the ghastly scenes toward the end where the hero Rubashov gradually disintegrates under the constant glare of voltage-lighting and confesses to crimes he never committed simply because he no longer cares. In the back of his mind is the inscription he saw over the grave of another political conspirator, DORMIR--to sleep.

It is trite to say that when a Russian mind lets itself go it has a humor and a controlled irony and a directed movement which are all its own. Maybe Mr. Koestler isn't Russian, I don't know; but this is the kind of thing we have learned to expect from, let us say, Chekhov or Gorki or Dostoevsky. It is the story of N. S. Rubashov, ex-commissar of the Soviet Republics, who was one of the founders of the Communist regime, served his red Republic abroad, unhesitatingly "liquidated" other secret agents

89B REVIEW BY CHRISTOPHER MORLEY

89. ARTHUR KOESTLER (b. 1905)

Darkness at Noon (1940)

A. First American edition. New York, 1941. Dust jacket. Put into English by Daphne Hardy.

B. Typed (carbon copy) review. 3pp. n.d. by Christopher Morley, who writes of "this powerful story":
> ". . . that it might be considered an essay on political psychology based on a famous quotation from Machiavelli which is reprinted as a motto . . . that it is required reading for anyone who may have wondered about the notorious Moscow Trials, and gives us the first intelligible comment on the pragmatic reasons behind them. And then, lest this discourage anyone, I hasten to say that it is brilliant reading and anyone who has an adequate chair and a good lamp will not rise until he finishes it."

C. Mimeograph play script by Sidney Kingsley based on the novel by Koestler. Blue wrappers with "Hart Stenographic Bureau" and New York address on front upper left. A. D. Peters, Literary Agent, label at lower right of title page. From the T. E. Hanley Collection.

90. W. H. AUDEN (b. 1907)

Another Time (1940)

A. First edition. New York, 1940. Dust jacket.

B. First English edition. London, 1940. Dust jacket.
From the library of Edith Sitwell with her markings throughout.
Proof copy, uncorrected. Original wrappers.

C. *Collected Shorter Poems 1930–1944.* London, 1950.
Dust jacket.
Includes *Another Time.*

D. Two holograph manuscripts with revisions, "Miss Gee" and "The Witness." n.d.

E. Holograph manuscript, "Poetical Ledger." 249pp. Drafts of poems, ideas and metric experiments written in America about 1953 and 1954. Auden gave this manuscript to Benjamin Britten, England's foremost composer with whom he collaborated on two symphonic cycles in 1936 and 1937 and an operetta in 1940. Britten presented it to the Aldeburgh Festival of Music and the Arts Committee to be sold to acquire funds for the purchase of a small property to be adapted for exhibitions.

90D HOLOGRAPH MANUSCRIPT

91. STEPHEN SPENDER (b. 1909)

Ruins and Visions (1942)

A. First edition. London, 1942. Dust jacket.
Proof copy, uncorrected. London, 1941. Original wrappers.

B. Holograph manuscript with emendations in ledger, "Sketches for poems in *Ruins & Visions*." 78pp. 1940.

C. Page proofs with extensive holograph corrections and additions by the author and signed by him on title page. Wrappers with typed note on front giving pages on which corrections and additions have been made.

D. First American edition. New York, 1942. Dust jacket.

E. Questionnaire *re* the rewards of being a poet sent to Spender by John Pudney with Spender's holograph replies signed. n.d.

F. Typescript, "Poetry for Poetry's Sake and Poetry Beyond Poetry" signed. 23pp. n.d. Spender begins by stating the hypothesis of a poem as
> "the emotional experience, the moment of vision, the flash of insight, the 'ligne donnée', the poetic logic which integrates a sequence of impressions and experiences around and in the light of an emotional conviction which has to be proved."

Critic as well as poet, he writes of his contemporaries Robert Graves, T. S. Eliot, W. H. Auden, Edith Sitwell, Dylan Thomas and others.

103

THE FATES

I

In the theatre,
The actors act the ritual of their parts,
Clowns, killers, lovers, captains,
At the end falling on the sword
Which opens a window through their hearts
And through the darkness to the gleaming eyes
Of those who watch, amused, thinking they're bored,
Where the audience
Act the part of their indifference,
Pretending the thrusting pistons of the passions,
Contorted masks of tears and mockery,
Do not penetrate the surface of the fashions
Covering their naked skins.

"We are not green fools nor black-eyed tragedians,
Though perhaps, long ago, we were the killers,
And even now we have our moments of romance
Under the moon, when we are the lovers,
But the rules of fate do not apply to us.

57

91C PROOF WITH AUTHOR'S CORRECTIONS

92. T. S. ELIOT (1888–1965)

Four Quartets (1943)

A. First edition. New York, 1943. Dust jacket.
Advance review copy. Tipped in, publisher's announcement on front free endpaper. Inscribed by Malcolm Cowley, with his annotations for review throughout. Dust jacket.

B. First English edition. London, 1944. Dust jacket.
Presentation copy inscribed: "to Edith Sitwell with the author's homage. T. S. Eliot 10.x.44."

C. Limited edition. London, 1960.
Number 21 of 290 copies signed by the author on paper made by Fratelli Magnani, Pescia. Printed in Dante type by Giovanni Mardersteig on the handpress of the Officina Bodoni in Verona. Eliot has lined out his name on the title page and written: "Inscribed for my friend the Revd William Turner Levy with apologies (he will know what for) by T. S. Eliot." Quarter vellum marbled boards, top edges gilt, and slip case.

D. First separate editions of the poems which make up *Four Quartets: East Coker*, 1940, *Burnt Norton, Dry Salvages*, 1941, *Little Gidding*, 1942, all in original wrappers. Although Eliot always intended the four poems to be published as one volume and to be judged as a single work, each first appeared separately. *East Coker* and *Burnt Norton* are from the library of A. E. Coppard, who has underlined words and phrases in pencil and placed emphatic punctuation marks and terse comments in the margins.

E. Corrected typescript, *The Dry Salvages*. 10pp. n.d. with a revised holograph version (1p.) of the last 18 lines, instructions to incorporate, and Eliot's initials in blue pencil. From the T. E. Hanley Collection.

F. Mimeograph copy, "T. S. Eliot" by John Lehmann 25 October 1947 with Lehmann's signature and note: "Talk Series for Far Eastern Programme. BBC." Lehmann comments on Eliot's work in general, noting particularly his "undeviating integrity of mind and poetic purpose . . . , seriousness and pertinacity" as well as the sureness of his literary growth and development which he likens to the unfolding of a "complex and beautiful flower . . . and *Four Quartets*, with its wonderful subtlety of structure, the harmony within its elaborate pattern . . . the supreme moment of full bloom."

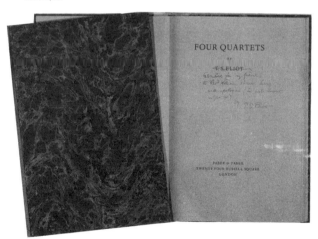

92C LIMITED EDITION INSCRIBED BY THE AUTHOR

93. GEORGE ORWELL (1903–1950)

Animal Farm (1945)

A. First edition. London, 1945. Dust jacket.
Presentation copy inscribed: "Rayner Heppenstall from Geo. Orwell." Laid in: one page from an exhibit catalogue "The Storyteller" with item 545 checked: "GEORGE ORWELL, pseudonym of ERIC BLAIR (1903–50). ANIMAL FARM. Secker and Warburg. 8vo. 1945. *Lent by the Publishers.*"

B. First American edition. New York, 1946. Dust jacket.

C. Ledger entitled "News Cuttings" with mimeograph script "George Orwell. Memories by his Sister, etc.," a BBC program produced by Rayner Heppenstall. 41pp. n.d. Arthur Koestler, who had met Orwell in 1941, participates in this program and tells how, about the middle of 1944 "before the flying bombs started," he had just finished lunch one day in a little place just off the Strand when Orwell rushed in and held out to him "a very slim slightly tatty brown-covered" typescript of his new book *Animal Farm* remarking: "It's about a lot of animals who revolt against the farmer—it's very anti-Russian. I don't think you're going to like it." Later, Koestler inquired about how the Russians had received the book. Orwell, says Koestler, replied with the same sort of dry humor which runs throughout the book that they had referred to him as a " 'Fascist beast . . . jackal . . . hyena,' and added in a sort of undertone—'I'm very fond of animals.' " This anecdote is marked out. From the T. E. Hanley Collection.

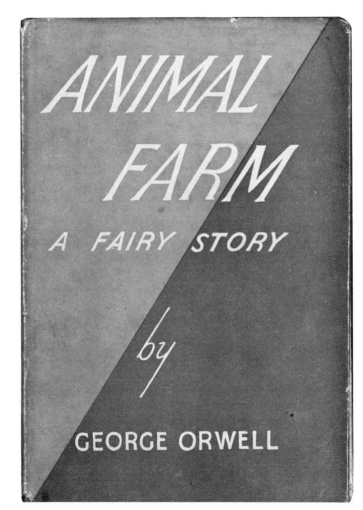

93A FIRST EDITION INSCRIBED BY THE AUTHOR

94. ALBERT CAMUS (1913–1960)

L'Étranger (1941)

A. First edition. Review copy. Paris, 1942.
Half burnt orange morocco, cork boards and end-papers. Original wrappers preserved.

B. Translation. *The Outsider*. London, 1946.
Put into English by Stuart Gilbert. Introduction by Cyril Connolly.

The Stranger. New York, 1946. Dust jacket.
Stuart Gilbert's translation without Connolly's introduction.

95. ALBERT CAMUS (1913–1960)

La peste (1947)

A. First edition. Paris, 1947.
One of 35 copies on *vélin*. Original wrappers.
Review copy. Paris, 1947.
Original wrappers. Laid in: author's card.

B. Illustrated edition. 2 volumes. Paris, 1962.
Illustrations by Edy-Legrand. Presentation copy inscribed by the artist to Blanche Knopf. Original decorated wrappers.

C. Translation. *The Plague*. New York, 1948. Dust jacket.
Put into English by Stuart Gilbert. Inscribed by Camus to Mr. and Mrs. [Alfred A.] Knopf.

English edition. London, 1948.

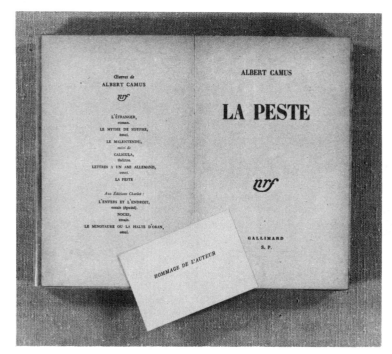

95A REVIEW COPY

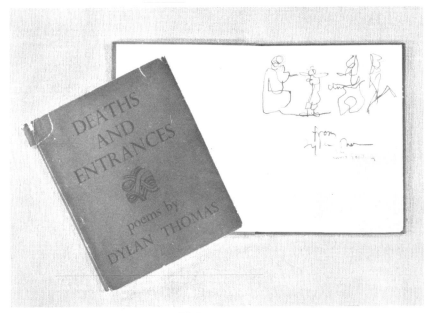

96(a)A FIRST EDITION INSCRIBED BY THE AUTHOR

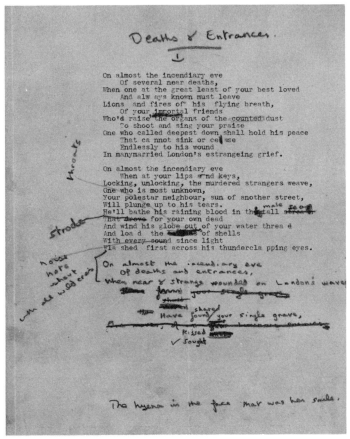

96(a)C TYPESCRIPT WITH AUTHOR'S CORRECTIONS
AND ADDITIONS

96. DYLAN THOMAS (1914–1953)

(a) *Deaths and Entrances* (1946)

A. First edition. London, 1946.
Presentation copy inscribed: "For Margaret and Alan [Taylor] with love from Dylan." Probably one of the earliest printed copies, as Thomas was living with the Taylors at this time. From the T. E. Hanley Collection.

Another copy. Dust jacket.
Thomas' grotesque figures in ink on front free endpaper. Inscribed: "From Dylan Thomas to Louis Golding." Perforation on back free endpaper: "Complimentary copy not for sale."

B. Reprint. London, 1949. Dust jacket.
With lines of "Vision and Prayer" pp. 43–44 beginning flush with the left margin and the entire copy marked in preparation for *Collected Poems* 1952.

C. Original manuscripts and typescripts of five poems: earliest known version of the title poem "Deaths and Entrances," "Lie Still, Sleep Bemused," "In My Craft Or Sullen Art," "Fern Hill," and an early version of "Poem (To Caitlin)."

(b) *New Poems* (1943)

A. First edition. Norfolk, Connecticut, 1943.
"Dora Douglas. Johannesburg, October, 1944" on front paste-down endpaper in Thomas' hand.
Another copy. Dust jacket.

B. Holograph manuscripts, "The Conversation Of Prayer," "On A Wedding Anniversary" with early printed version, and "Among Those Killed In The Dawn Raid Was A Man Aged A Hundred" inscribed: "To Charles From Dylan in Bradford" and accompanied by a long typed note revealing the circumstances under which the poem was written. Typed name and a date: "Charles de Latour, London, March 30, 1954."

C. Holograph manuscript with extensive revisions, "How To Be A Poet." 12pp. n.d. Accompanied by holograph note signed by John Davenport 5 April 1955. Originally written in 1949 as a lecture to be delivered to a literary society in Swansea, Thomas showed it to Davenport who immediately claimed it for his magazine *Circus* which was about to appear. It was published in two parts in the first and second numbers (the magazine was discontinued after the third) with illustrations by Ronald Searle. Thomas originally titled the essay "Poetry As A Career." The first page carries a note at upper left: "Your Editor, in a moment of over-confidence, has invited me to talk about this subject." The first paragraph referring to the lecture has been lined out. From the T. E. Hanley Collection.

97. JOHN BETJEMAN (b. 1906)

Selected Poems (1948)

A. First edition. London, 1948.

Chosen and with a preface by John Sparrow, who comments on the nature and quality of Betjeman's poetry—poetry that is inspired by what Betjeman calls "topographical predilection." His poems describe a scene or convey the atmosphere of a place, figures are subordinate to their setting. Even when a story is told, incidents seem designed "to make the landscape articulate, to give a voice . . . to the atmosphere of the Lincolnshire fens or the lakes of Westmeath or the London suburbs." He finds matter for poetry in the least promising surroundings—the suburbs, the city, gaslights, churches, railways. He sees them through the eyes of those who build them as well as of those who inhabit them and emphasizes the fact that this in itself adds something new to poetry. From the library of Evelyn Waugh with his bookplate.

B. Galley proofs headed *Collected Poems* for *Selected Poems* 1948. Corrected by Betjeman.

C. Exercise book with poems in holograph including "Dorset" and "The Arrest of Oscar Wilde at the Cadogan Hotel." n.d.

D. Original holograph manuscript of "May Day Song for North Oxford" with water color drawing. The first two verses of this poem appear in *Selected Poems* as "Spring Morning in North Oxford." Given to Cyril Connolly by John Betjeman when the poem was first printed in *Horizon*.

E. *A Few Late Chrysanthemums*. London. 1954.

Number 13 of an autographed edition limited to 50 copies. Cited by Connolly as containing some of Betjeman's best poems.

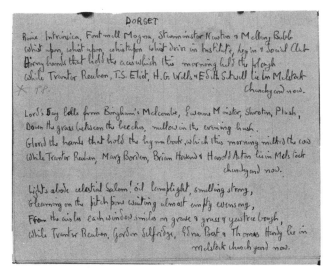

97C EXERCISE BOOK WITH POEMS IN HOLOGRAPH

98. EZRA POUND (b. 1885)

The Pisan Cantos (1948)

A. First edition. New York, 1948. Dust jacket.
From the library of E. E. Cummings with Cummings' name and address embossed on front free endpaper. Photograph of Pound laid in.

B. First English edition. London, 1949. Dust jacket.
From the library of John Heath-Stubbs with his signature on front free endpaper.

C. Holograph manuscript, "Homage to Ezra Pound on his Seventieth Birthday" by Edith Sitwell, signed. 1p. n.d. Reading in part:
> "To the miraculous beauty of vision and image of the transcendental Second Canto, and of that marvellous passage about the lynxes and the maelids and bassarids in Canto LXXIX of the Pisan Cantos; to the flute-music of the short lyrics that would certainly—to transcribe one passage in Canto XIII keep the blossoms of the apricots from falling—we pay homage.
> "To the great creator of these we pay homage, and to him whose influence on the best poetry of our time has been a creative force."

99. GEORGE ORWELL (1903–1950)

Nineteen Eighty-Four (1949)

A. First edition. London, 1949.
Evelyn Waugh's copy with his bookplate.

B. First American edition. New York, 1949.

C. Advance review copy. New York, 1949. Wrappers.

D. Series of letters from Orwell to Rayner Heppenstall 1939–1946 some typed, some holograph, several on *The Tribune* letterhead. Early letters signed Eric Blair; those after 1940 George Orwell. He congratulates Heppenstall 16 April 1940 on the birth of a child and cautions him about names and their effect upon a child's personality, concluding: "It took me nearly thirty years to work off the effects of being called Eric."

100. WILLIAM CARLOS WILLIAMS (1883–1963)

Paterson, 1, 2, 3, 4, 5 (1946–1958)

A. First editions:
Book One. New York, 1946.
Advance review copy. Tipped in: New Directions card with typed inscription: "E. E. Cummings Compliments of W. C. Williams."

Book Two. New York, 1948. Dust jacket.
Signed by the author.

Book Three. New York, 1949. Dust jacket.
Signed by the author.

Book Four. New York, 1951. Dust jacket.
Signed by the author.

Book Five. New York, 1958. Dust jacket.
Presentation copy inscribed: "Gratefully to Julian Beck from his friend William Carlos Williams."

B. Collected edition. Books I–V. London, 1964. Dust jacket.

C. Six typed letters from a series dating from March 1946 to April 1950 signed by Williams to Bonnie Golightly, a young writer on the contemporary literary scene. The letters, written during the *Paterson* period, are both literary and personal. Also, holograph note on prescription pad paper to John Hermann, friend and fellow-writer. n.d.

D. Typed letter signed by Williams 15 March 1939 in response to an inquiry concerning the definition of poetry he had given at the Munson studio. After explaining that he cannot remember his precise words but what he has in mind had remained stable for a number of years and may therefore serve, he continues:

"The poet's task, in any age, is to listen to the language of his time, when it is impassioned and wherever it occurs, and to discover in it, from it, the essentials of his form, *his* form, as of his own day. From these essentials he makes up his patterns —embodying the characteristics of what he finds alive in his day. The [*sic*] is the task of the major poet in any time.

"The secondary task which a poet assumes is to jam the tide of his day into the forms of the past. This is what is usually understood by 'poet.' It is safe, it is respectable, it is easy to understand and —it stinks.

"Poetry should be the synthesis of its time in passionately communicable form. . . ."

Acknowledgments

The University of Texas at Austin is indebted to the following persons and firms for permission to quote from the letters and works which appear in this catalog: Mr. W. H. Auden: W. H. AUDEN / Mr. Rupert Hart-Davis and Mrs. Eva Reichmann: MAX BEERBOHM / John Murray Publishers: JOHN BETJEMAN / Mr. Richard Church: RICHARD CHURCH / Mr. Edouard Dermit: JEAN COCTEAU / Mr. Anthony Compton-Burnett: IVY COMPTON-BURNETT / Mr. Cyril Connolly: CYRIL CONNOLLY / J. M. Dent & Sons Ltd. and the Trustees of the Joseph Conrad Estate: JOSEPH CONRAD / Mr. Samuel Loveman: HART CRANE / Mr. Armitage Watkins: HARRY and CARESSE CROSBY / Society of Authors on behalf of the estates of NORMAN DOUGLAS, E. M. FORSTER, JAMES JOYCE, LYTTON STRACHEY / Mrs. T. S. Eliot: T. S. ELIOT / New Directions Publishing Corporation: RICHARD ELLMANN (from his introduction to Henri Michaux, *Selected Writings* ©1968), EZRA POUND, ROGER SHATTUCK (from his introduction to Guillaume Apollinaire *Selected Writings* [1948]), DYLAN THOMAS (from *Collected Poems* ©1943). / Col. Thomas Firbank: RONALD FIRBANK / Janice Biala: FORD MADOX FORD / Mr. Robert Graves: ROBERT GRAVES / Mr. Henry Green: HENRY GREEN / Mr. Graham Greene: GRAHAM GREENE / William Heinemann Ltd. Publishers: WILLIAM HEINEMANN / Mrs. Ernest Hemingway: ERNEST HEMINGWAY / Oxford University Press on behalf of the Society of Jesus: GERARD MANLEY HOPKINS / Harper & Row Publishers, Inc.: ALDOUS HUXLEY, PETER QUENNELL / Mrs. Laura Huxley: ALDOUS HUXLEY / Mr. Christopher Isherwood: CHRISTOPHER ISHERWOOD / Mr. Alexander R. James: HENRY JAMES / Laurence Pollinger Limited on behalf of the estates of D. H. and FRIEDA LAWRENCE / Mr. A. W. Lawrence: T. E. LAWRENCE / Mr. John Lehmann: JOHN LEHMANN / Mr. A. D. MacCarthy: DESMOND MACCARTHY / Mr. E. R. Dodds and Mrs. Hedli MacNeice: LOUIS MACNEICE / Mrs. Blythe Morley Brennan: CHRISTOPHER MORLEY / Mrs. Mary Middleton Murray: KATHERINE MANSFIELD / Mr. John Warner Moore: MARIANNE MOORE / Harcourt Brace Jovanovich, Inc.: GEORGE ORWELL (*The Collected Essays, Journalism and Letters of George Orwell*, Volume 2) / David Higham Associates, Ltd.: EDITH SITWELL / Mr. John Sparrow: JOHN SPARROW / Mr. Stephen Spender: STEPHEN SPENDER / Alfred A. Knopf, Inc.: WALLACE STEVENS (*Letters of Wallace Stevens* Selected and Edited by Holly Stevens, ©1966 by Holly Stevens) / Oxford University Press: VILLIERS DE L'ISLE-ADAM / Harold Ober Associates, Incorporated: DYLAN THOMAS (©1970 by The Trustees for the Copyrights of Dylan Thomas), F. SCOTT FITZGERALD / Mrs. Arthur Waley: ARTHUR WALEY / A. D. Peters & Co.: EVELYN WAUGH / Hogarth Press and the Executor of the Estate of Virginia Woolf: VIRGINIA WOOLF / Mr. M. B. Yeats: W. B. YEATS / Mrs. Florence H. Williams: WILLIAM CARLOS WILLIAMS.

I wish to express my special thanks to Mr. Cyril Connolly, whose book *The Modern Movement: 100 Key Books from England, France and America 1880–1950* provided the inspiration for this catalog, to the several scholars who so graciously read the script and offered helpful advice and suggestions, and to the many who viewed portions of the exhibit in progress and provided day-by-day encouragement.

MARY HIRTH

May 1971

Index

119

This catalog has been printed on Adena Eggshell.
The type is Linotype Caledonia for the text with Sistina and
Palatino for the titling. Design by William R. Holman.